SILENT SPEECH AND SILENT READING

SILENT SPEECH

AND

SILENT READING

by

ÅKE W. EDFELDT

THE UNIVERSITY OF CHICAGO PRESS

Library of Congress Catalog Number 60–8125

THE UNIVERSITY OF CHICAGO PRESS, CHICAGO 37

Cambridge University Press, London, N.W. 1, England

The University of Toronto Press, Toronto 5, Canada

Published 1960 by The University of Chicago Press.

Printed in Sweden by

Ivar Hæggströms Boktryckeri AB

Stockholm 1960

PREFACE

One of the intriguing problems that for decades has baffled research workers in the field of reading, relates to the extent to which inner speech, or movements of the muscles of the speech mechanism, occur during silent reading. Early in the current century, Edmund B. Huey called attention to their presence but pointed out serious limitations in the evidence available concerning them. He adopted the view, however, that to the extent that they do occur, they aid the reader in keeping in mind the various elements of meaning until he receives a clear grasp of the idea intended by the author.

During the decades that followed, several investigators endeavored to secure more detailed and accurate evidence concerning the extent of silent speech during silent reading. Their findings have been conflicting and inconclusive due to the inadequacy of the methods used in identifying muscle movements of the speech mechanism during silent reading. Those who favored the view that such movements are an invariable accompaniment of silent reading, did so on the assumptions that meanings and language are so intimately related that silent reading cannot occur without inner speech. Others maintained that the presence of speech movements are not essential and are the result of inappropriate methods used in teaching reading. In harmony with the latter view, efforts have been made in some schools to prevent the development of inner speech while reading through the use of non-oral methods of teaching reading. Studies made of the reading habits of children taught by non-oral methods showed that lip movements occurred almost as much among them as among those who had been taught to read through the use of the usual methods. For these and other reasons issues relating to the extent, causes, and practical implications of inner speech have persisted.

v

The study reported by Dr. Edfeldt in this volume represents a different and more valid approach to the identification of silent speech during silent reading. Following a critical review of previous investigations, supplemented by preliminary research of his own, he made use of electromyographic methods in identifying movements of the speech muscles. The records thus secured revealed new and illuminating facts concerning the extent of silent speech during silent reading. Of special significance are his conclusions that silent speech is *probably* universal during silent reading that it increases with the difficulty of the material read, and that efforts to eliminate it through instruction should be discontinued. His findings leave unanswered such questions as the relation of inner speech to comprehension. Fortunately, however, the validity of a new technique for use in further research has been established. Through his efforts, Dr. Edfeldt has also established a new milepost in our understanding of both the extent and practical implications of inner speech and has suggested a series of issues as a guide to further research in this field.

William S. Gray

"...we believed that the divisions between the sciences were convenient administrative lines for the apportionment of money and effort, which each working scientist should be willing to cross whenever his studies should appear to demand it. Science, we both felt, should be a collaborative effort."

> (Norbert Wiener concerning his working relationship with Arturo Rosenblueth, the Mexican neurologist as described in *I Am a Mathematician*.)

ACKNOWLEDGMENTS

This investigation has involved constant crossing of boundaries between experimental educational psychology and other areas of knowledge, above all medicine. I wish therefore to express my gratitude to those specialists in different fields who have given me advice and guidance concerning various specific problems. In particular, this gratitude is due Docent Sven Carlsöö and Rune Elmqvist, M.D., of Stockholm and K. Faaborg-Andersen, M.D., of Nykøbing (Falster), Denmark, at whose ear, nose and throat clinic my basic methodological study was conducted. In this latter regard, I wish as well to proffer my thanks to the administration of the Central Hospital in Nykøbing (Falster), Denmark for the time I spent there at Dr. Faaborg-Andersen's clinic, as a guest of the hospital.

In the clinical part of the Stockholm investigation, the insertion of the electrodes was skillfully carried out by Ingemar Bramme, M.B., of Stockholm.

In certain epistemological questions, I have had the benefit of a discussion with Professor H. Thörnebom of the University of Khartoum, Sudan.

Docent Sten Henrysson and Lars Andersson, assistant statistician, both of Stockholm, have given me assistance regarding the statistical treatment of the experimental results.

On technical problems, I have benefitted from the advice of Dr. Rune Elmqvist and from that of Lars Ericsson, electrical engineer, of Stockholm, who has also constructed the integrator unit used in the experiments.

The translation into English of this dissertation has been produced by Jack Wright, B.A., of Kungsängen.

To all of the above, I wish to express my gratitude for their valuable help.

For many years, at the University of Stockholm, I have had the pleasure of gaining, at the hands of my instructors and colleagues, increased knowledge which has been useful to me in my work. I particularly wish to thank Professor Arne Trankell who has been my instructor and advisor during all phases of the work on this investigation.

It has been possible to carry out this work thanks to research grants from Association Scandinavia ("Föreningen Norden"), the Arts Faculty of the University of Stockholm ("Humanistiska fakulteten vid Stockholms högskola"), the Längman Cultural Fund ("Längmanska kulturfonden"), the Magnus Bergvall Foundation ("Magnus Bergvalls stiftelse"), the State Institute of Educational Psychology ("Statens psykologisk-pedagogiska institut") and the periodical "Our School" ("Vår skola").

University of Stockholm
Educational Department
Institute of Reading Research
May 1959

Åke W. Edfeldt

CONTENTS

Preface v

Acknowledgements vii

Contents 5
    Tables 7
    Figures 9

Introduction 11

Part I. Research concerning the usability of the electromyographic method in a study of silent speech 13

    Chapter 1. Silent speech as a problem of fundamental research   13

        Early experimental studies on silent speech   15

    Chapter 2. Preparatory experiments by the present author employing methods used by earlier investigators   30

        Recording devices and method   30
        Results and discussion   32

    Chapter 3. The electromyographic method   36

    Chapter 4. A description of certain parts of the organ of speech   46

        The larynx   46
        Anatomy and function of some muscles used in speech   48

    Chapter 5. Electromyographic experiments on different parts of the organ of speech   50

        Earlier investigations by other experimenters and first experiments by the present author   50

        Recordings from the larynx   50
        Recordings from other parts of the speech musculature   52

        Experiments performed to establish the method later to be used in the main investigation by the present author   57

        The problem in the Denmark investigation   57
        Apparatus, method and subjects   58
        Results and discussion   65

Part II. Silent speech in applied research on reading and an experimental contribution employing the electromyographic method   75

Chapter 6. Theories concerning the nature of silent speech in
   reading   75

  The occurrence of silent speech   77
  Conceivable causes of silent speech   79
  The effects of silent speech   87
  Elimination of silent speech   92
  Setting of the hypotheses of the Stockholm in-
  vestigation   103

Chapter 7. The Stockholm investigation   110

  Apparatus used in the experiment   111
  The experimental subjects   114
  Plan of the various parts of the experiment   115
  The conduct of the electromyographic experiments
  and their results   118
  Correlations between silent speech and some other
  experimental variables   136

Chapter 8. Discussion and conclusions   140

  Testing the experimental hypotheses   144
   Hypothesis A   144
   Hypothesis B   145
   Hypothesis C   145

  Bearings of the present experimental results on earlier
  theories   146

Chapter 9. Summary   153

Appendix A. Silent speech and the diagnosis of individual reading
ability   155

References   160

TABLES (NUMBERED)

Part I.

1. Experimental results adopted from Reed 20
2. Experimental results adopted from Pintner 22
3. Pattern of tongue movements during whispering and during
   internal speech. A comparison made by Thorson 25
4. Pattern of tongue movements during repetition of the same
   tasks in internal speech. A comparison made by Thorson 26
5. Pattern of tongue movements during repeated whispering of
   the same tasks. A comparison made by Thorson 26
6. Reading test results and bioelectric activity in standard scores 70
7. Reading points and silent speech points 72
8. Final experimental results of the Denmark investigation 73

Part II.

9. Reading rates (oral and silent reading) of pupils in the Boston
   University Educational Clinic. Adopted from Durrell 87
10. Data concerning the reading tests used 115
11. Results of the F-tests made on values from reading period I . 125
12. Summary of the results appearing in Table 11 126
13. Same data as in Table 12, but arranged for χ^2-test 127
14. Analysis of variance on A-quotients from reading period I .. 128
15. Analysis of variance on A-differences from reading period I . 129
16. Analysis of variance on square root transformations of the A-
    quotients from reading period I 130
17. Analysis of variance on A-quotients from reading period II . 131
18. Analysis of variance on A-differences from reading period II 132
19. p-values of all the sources of variance from the analyses of
    variance appearing in Tables 14-18 133
20. Testing the changes in silent speech in transitions from one
    text to another: 1 134
21. Testing the changes in silent speech in transitions from one
    text to another: 2 135
22. Coefficients of correlation between silent speech and certain
    other variables in elementary school subjects 137
23. Coefficients of correlation between silent speech and the
    reading variables: the Stockholm investigation 138
24. Coefficients of correlation between silent speech and the in-
    telligence test results: the Stockholm investigation 138

25. Coefficients of correlation betwc:en eye-movement variables
    and the reading variables: the Stockholm investigation 139
26. Coefficients of correlation between eye-movement variables
    and silent speech: the Stockholm investigation 139

Appendix A

27. Coefficients of correlation between A-differences and reading
    scores in the reading ability groups taken separately 156

TEXT-TABLES (NOT NUMBERED)

A complete experimental run from the Denmark investigation .. 61
Electrode combinations used in the Denmark investigation 63
McDade's experimental results 94
The number of vocalizers among Buswell's subjects 96
A complete experimental run from the Stockholm investigation .. 121
Key to Table 11 126
Intercorrelations between auxiliary movements in reading 137
The influence of intelligence on silent speech in reading: university
    students as subjects 159
The influence of intelligence on silent speech in reading: elementary
    school pupils as subjects 159

FIGURES

Part I.

Fig.

1. Experimental results obtained by Curtis 16
2. Parts of Reed's experimental apparatus 18
3. Thorson's experimental apparatus ($\times$ 0.5) 25
4. Experimental device used by the present author to pick up impulses from the tongue 31
5a. Record taken from subject X during relaxation 33
5b. Record taken from the same subject during silent recitation . 33
5c. Record taken from the same subject during reading 33
6. Differences in electromyograms obtained during muscular contractions of different strengths (from Buchtal) 38
7. Different patterns in electromyograms (from Buchtal) 39
8. Changes in an electromyogram during increasing contraction of a muscle, according to Wegener 42
9. A direct and an integrated electromyogram (from Inman et al.) 43
10. Activity in the vocal muscle and in the cricothyroid muscle during phonation, silent speech and relaxation (from Faaborg-Andersen) 51
11. Different types of electrodes used by Kratin 53
12. A record of silent speech, according to Faaborg-Andersen 56
13. The concentric needle electrode 60
14. The bipolar needle electrode 60
15. Electric activity in the vocal and the mylohyoid muscles during reading 66
16. Electric activity in the vocal muscle during reading 69
17. Electric activity in the posterior cricoarytenoid muscle during reading 71

Part II.

18. Buswell's experimental results 95
19. Diagram of our integrator unit 111
20. Picture of all the amplifying units employed 113
21. Recording obtained with our experimental apparatus from the gluteus maximus muscle during decreasing contraction 114
22. Distribution of reading results in z-scores and dividing lines between the three reading ability groups 116
23. The opening lines of the four texts used in reading periods I-IV 117

9

24. Over-all view of the experimental equipment 119
25. Specimen of relaxation curve 123
26. Specimen of reading activity curve 123
27. Average growth in reading ability as measured by total com-
    prehension score in Chicago Reading Test D, Form 2 (grades
    III to XIII) 149

Appendix A

28. Single diphasic spike potentials; b shows two such spike
    potentials in opposite phases 158

INTRODUCTION

The present work constitutes an attempt to tackle an old problem in reading research by means of a method which has not been used earlier in experimental educational psychology. In medical research, the method has become well known as an aid in many different types of investigations. This fact, that the experimental method used has been borrowed from another area of knowledge, has left its mark both on the investigation itself and on the present report. The description of the electromyographic method which constitutes Chapter 3 has thus attained greater length than would have been the case if the method were one more commonly used in psychological research.

The introductory chapters contain a review of earlier research on silent speech generally (Chapter 1) and a report of our own experiments utilizing methods very similar to those employed in this earlier research (Chapter 2). The description of the electromyographic method and a description of the larynx and of certain muscles used in speech then follow as Chapters 3 and 4, respectively. Chapter 5, which concludes Part I, consists of a report on our basic methodological experiment performed in Denmark and its results.

Part II commences with a review of theories and views concerning the occurrence of silent speech in reading (Chapter 6). This chapter concludes with the setting of the hypotheses to be tested in the main experiment, the Stockholm investigation. A description of the main experiment and its results are given in Chapter 7, while Chapter 8 contains the discussion of these results as well as the conclusions which may be drawn from them. Chapter 9 consists of a brief summary of the whole investigation. The value for diagnoses of reading ability of our observations, during the Stockholm investigation, concerning silent speech in reading is then treated in an appendix (Appendix A). A list of references concludes the study.

Research Concerning the Usability of the Electromyographic Method in a Study of Silent Speech

---

CHAPTER 1

SILENT SPEECH AS A PROBLEM OF FUNDAMENTAL RESEARCH

A phenomenon which has long been subject to discussion in connection with thinking is silent speech. Thus, we find similar statements regarding the process of thought on the part of Alexander Bain and Théodule Ribot in the latter part of the nineteenth century. They consider thinking to be more or less restrained speaking or acting. Bain (1868) developed this idea in a chapter concerned with retentiveness and which included, in part, statements concerning the support which memory has from inner speech (p. 336 et seqq.).

The phenomenon has many names: silent speech, inner speech and internal speech are used in the literature available on the subject more or less synonymously with such terms as subvocalization and vocalization. The term "silent speech" expresses most adequately that which the present author considers to be included in the concept "movements in the speech musculature in accompaniment with reading[1] or other forms of mental activity," since all degrees of accompanying move-

---

[1] We wish here to make clear that the term "reading," when used in the present work, refers always to *silent* reading. When we have occasion to speak of reading aloud, we shall specifically refer to it as "oral reading." In statements where we are obliged to refer to both these types of reading, e.g., in comparing them with each other, we shall specify by means of the terms "silent reading" and "oral reading."

ments must here be included, from visible lip movements to those movements, in the speech muscles, which are completely inaccessible to simple observation. Therefore, *we shall henceforth use the term "silent speech" for all instances of movement in the speech muscles in accompaniment with reading or other forms of mental activity. In reporting on the opinions of other authors, however, we shall adhere to the terms which they use, respectively.*

It is impossible to discuss silent speech in reading independent of the early theories on silent speech in thinking. The discussion started from two diametrically opposed viewpoints which may be represented here by S. S. Stricker (1880) and M. Paulhan (1886). Both base their work on pure introspection, their own as well as that of other persons. Stricker and his subjects claim that they cannot think of letters or words without experiencing corresponding speech-motor phenomena. According to Stricker, even when he tried to recite aloud a poem of Schiller's which he had learned by heart, at the same time that he read silently a newspaper article, the speech movements which accompanied the reading broke through between the words of the poem.

In opposition to Stricker, Paulhan claimed that he could think of absolutely anything without experiencing accompanying speech-motor phenomena. It is unclear whether Paulhan actually meant that inner speech is a phenomenon peculiar to certain individuals, or that it does not exist at all. Both viewpoints could be drawn from his written report.

Among others who dealt with the question by means of the introspective method were the French psychologists, Egger (1881) and Ballet (1886), both of whom were primarily concerned with the aphasia problem. When they, in this connection, investigated normal speaking and reading abilities, they arrived also at the question of the importance of inner speech. The viewpoints of both authors may be characterized by the following quotation from Egger: *"Lire, en effet, c'est traduire l'écriture en parole"* (p. 1). (To read, as a matter of fact, is to translate the written text into words to be spoken.)

14

To this need only be added that Ballet particularly emphasized the importance that hearing has for reading.

Since the beginning of this dispute which was thus, to a large extent, originally based on subjective methods of control, different experimenters have tried, objectively, to clear up the problem.

Early Experimental Studies on Silent Speech

An objection which has repeatedly been made to the introspective method is that the phenomenon which is observed is altered in the very process of its being consciously observed. This of course applies, to a very great extent, to silent speech. In this particular case, therefore, it might be supposed that an outside observer, instead, could watch for and see the different movements which constitute silent speech. That not even this is necessarily true was shown by Hansen and Lehman (1895) in their experiments on mind reading. They found that a person who thought intently of a number or word almost always produced an unconscious whispering, and that this whispering could be heard by an observer who stood in such a position that the acoustics of the room particularly favored him. No one was able to observe any movements whatsoever on the lips of the whisperer. Since it is impossible to whisper without the muscles of articulation working, Hansen and Lehman considered that they had demonstrated that this muscle activity can occur without either the subject or observers around him being aware of the slightest movement.

Curtis (1899) placed a tambour on the larynx and thus recorded its movements. Among the curves which were registered, those for reading (of *Hiawatha*) are of particular interest. These indicated for 15 of the 20 experimental subjects considerably more movement than for other kinds of mental activity. Only the curves for actual whispering gave more extreme results, as is indicated, for example, in Fig. 1. Four of Curtis's cases showed no movement at all. Pintner (1913) comments on these cases, as follows (p. 136):

15

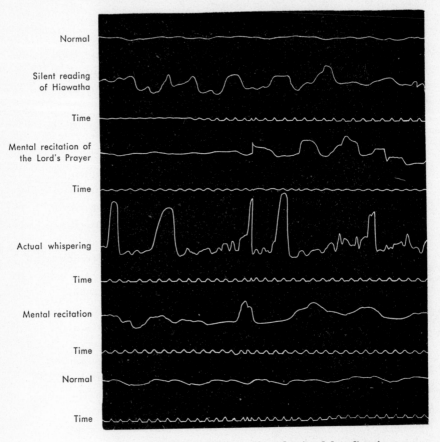

Normal

Silent reading
of Hiawatha

Time

Mental recitation of
the Lord's Prayer

Time

Actual whispering

Time

Mental recitation

Time

Normal

Time

Fig. 1. Experimental results obtained by Curtis.

The conclusion from these five[1] is a negative one. In all probability articulatory movements were present, but the instruments used were not delicate enough to record them. Again the larynx is not the only organ brought into play by articulation, and it is possible that in many cases the anatomical build of the neck prevents direct movements of the larynx being recorded.

---

[1] There is a misunderstanding here on the part of Pintner, as one of these five subjects had been instructed to suppress, to the greatest extent possible, all movements. (See Curtis, p. 239.)

In line with Curtis's results are those obtained by Courten (1902) in experiments where movements of the tongue, however, rather than of the larynx, were recorded, during the performance of the same activities as those on which Curtis experimented. Courten worked with a rubber bulb on the tongue, the bulb being connected with a recording tambour.

During the 1890's, there were many different investigators who conducted experiments involving different kinds of distraction intended to hinder silent speech. Among those who worked in this field can be mentioned Münsterberg, W. G. Smith, Th. L. Smith, Breese and Secor. No definite conclusions were obtained from these experiments, other than that silent speech was relatively universal and seemed to have an influence on the mental activities which it accompanied. Greater stress on the connection between reading and silent speech, however, is to be found, for example, in the work of Huey (1908).

All the experiments mentioned hitherto were conducted with apparatus which was really more suitable for the measurement of muscular activity accompanying ordinary speech. Such was also the case with the apparatus which Tomor (1910) used to determine whether there were accompanying movements in the lips, tongue or larynx in connection with thinking. Although the movements indicated by his apparatus were not very great as compared with those indicated for speech, he nevertheless considered them sufficient to permit him to state that all thinking is accomplished by activity in the musculature of these organs. He was also of the opinion that this activity might be the true explanation of the fact that even mental work can produce a condition of tiredness.

Wyczoikowska (1913) discussed the connection between tongue movements and movements of the right thumb of her subjects.[1] In the same report, she describes an experiment in

---

[1] A part of her report gives a description of how a common nerve branches off both to the thumb and to the tongue. She claims that an anatomical basis is thus provided for the phenomenon of pressure upon the thenary eminence of the right thumb resulting, in one case, in the appearance of a cavity on the tongue.

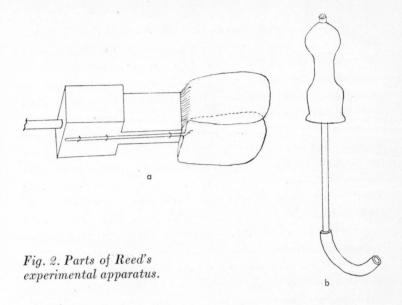

Fig. 2. Parts of Reed's experimental apparatus.

b

which tongue movements only were measured. She had her subjects try to solve certain mental problems or simply think of a certain phrase over and over again, while their tongue movements were recorded via a flattened glass cup ("a sort of flattened wine glass as a receiver," p. 453), which, by means of a rubber tube, was connected to a recording tambour. The results of her experiments caused her to suppose that every act of thought was accompanied by movements of the tongue.

Another attempt to solve the problem experimentally was made by H. B. Reed (1916). He took recordings from the tongue movements of his subjects by means of a specially constructed drum, as shown in Fig. 2 a. A condom of very thin rubber was stretched over the steel wires seen in the figure. When the subject took the drum in his mouth, closed his lips and bit down on the wooden framework, which was placed between the teeth, the rubber membrane of the drum reacted to all changes of air pressure in the mouth cavity. Through the recording tube, seen furthest to the left in the figure, these changes in air pressure were led for kymographic registration.

18

As these changes in air pressure in the drum would not be due to silent speech alone, but also to ordinary breathing movements, the latter had to be controlled, as well. This was achieved (simultaneously with the drum recording and kymographic registration) partly in the usual way by means of a pneumograph and partly through the recording of expiration through the nose by means of Raymond Dodge's recording tambour shown in Fig. 2 b. On each of his subjects, Reed conducted experiments from which he registered the following types of graphic records:

1. breathing curve (the subjects tried to relax)
2. silent reading curve (brief newspaper clipping)
3. writing curve (review of a brief newspaper clipping)
4. whispering curve (same brief newspaper clipping)
5. oral reading curve (same brief newspaper clipping).

He also made recordings during "mental counting, mental multiplying and addition." A comparison of a part of the graphic records, on the one hand, and introspective reports from his 13 subjects, on the other, gave the results indicated in Table 1.

On the basis of these results, Reed concludes that inner speech is an individual peculiarity of certain persons. A further conclusion drawn by Reed is that introspective reports alone are unreliable as a source of scientific data (since the agreements between graphic record and introspective report constitute only $5/8$ of the total number of cases, whereas the remaining $3/8$ are instances of disagreement or uncertainty). Reed adds, concerning the first conclusion (op. cit., p. 381):

The discovery that inner speech is an individual trait does not tell us what its function is. If we could find a uniform set of circumstances in which it always appeared, we should be able to infer its function. But the facts seem to be that most people who use it at all, use it in every mental process. A few who do not use it in simple processes, use it in difficult processes. Many do not use it at all.

Reed then attempted, with the aid of a distraction experiment, to determine whether or not inner speech was of any importance for the thought activity of those persons who gave

19

Table 1. Experimental results adopted from Reed (1916, p. 381).

+ = process in question[1] is used. — = process in question[1] is not used.

Subject	Silent reading Graphic record	Silent reading Introspection	Writing Graphic record	Writing Introspection	Mental counting Graphic record	Mental counting Introspection	Mental multiplying Graphic record	Mental multiplying Introspection	Addition Graphic record	Addition Introspection
Mr. D	+	+	+	+	+	+	+	+	+	+
Mr. E	—	—	+	?	—	—	—	—	—	—
Mr. A	—	+	—	+	—	—	+	+	+	+
Mr. B	—	?	+	?	—	?	—	?	—	?
Mr. C	+	—	—	—			—	—	+	—
Mrs. E	—	—·	+	+						
Mr. Mc	—	—	+	− ?	—	—	?	?	+	?
Mr. M	—	—	+	+	—	—	?	—	?	+
Mr. Mt	+	+	+	+	+	+	+	+	+·	+
Dr. P	+	+ +	+	+						
Mrs. R	—	—	+	?	—	—	?	—	?	—
Dr. S	—	—	—	?	—	—	?	—	—	+
Mrs. W	—	—	—	—						
	4 + 9 —	4 + 8 — 1 ?	9 + 4 —	6 + 2 — 5 ?	2 + 7 —	2 + 6 — 1 ?	3 + 3 — 4 ?	3 + 5 — 2 ?	5 + 3 — 2 ?	5 + 3 — 2 ?

[1] Reed means here "inner speech."

some indication of using it. The element of distraction in the experiment was that the subjects, while performing the same tasks as described earlier (reading and writing reviews of newspaper clippings), were to repeat aloud and without interruption the sentence: "Jack and Jill ran down the hill." Careful tests were conducted regarding the subjects' reading and writing speeds and regarding their reading comprehension. These tests indicated that the achievement of some of the subjects who experienced inner speech introspectively improved during the distraction, whereas the achievement of others worsened. On the basis of these experiments, Reed concludes (op. cit., p. 390):

The general conclusion which the tests in connection with the newspaper clippings point to is that inner speech has no important function in comprehension in reading, and in writing, or in the rate of reading and writing.

Pintner (op.cit.) had also made a series of tests designed to show the extent to which silent speech could be influenced by disturbances. More than a hundred reading paragraphs were selected from such publications as *The American Magazine*, and the content of each paragraph was divided into ten units, "points," in the same way as in certain memory experiments. Each paragraph included about 70 words, the variation range being 60-79 words. Two different subjects, "observers," read all the paragraphs, their reading times being recorded. Their reports on the content of the respective paragraphs were made in writing, in all cases, immediately following the reading of each separate paragraph. As both the speed of reading and the reading comprehension were to be taken into consideration, the results for each paragraph were transformed into "reading values," obtained by dividing the percentage of points retained by the reading time.

The reading of the different paragraphs proceeded according to the following schedule:

a) some trials (to allow the observer to get accustomed to the method)
b) 20 timed readings
c) 7 series of 9 paragraphs each, while the observer repeated in an audible voice: "thirteen, fourteen, fifteen, sixteen" (altogether, 63 readings)
d) 20 timed readings (d = b).

Table 2 shows the results which Pintner obtained for the two observers he used.

On the basis of these results and of the introspective reports which Pintner received from his observers A and B, he summarized his conclusions, as follows (pp. 152-153):

1. That articulation during the reading process is a habit, which is not necessary for that process.

Table 2. Experimental results adopted from Pintner
(1913, p. 148).

Groups	Observer A		Observer B	
	Time	Reading value	Time	Reading value
Ordinary before	31.6	1.0	18.0	3.0
Inhibition				
Group A	31.6	0.7	22.9	1.1
Group B	27.2	1.0	20.0	2.0
Group C	26.6	0.9	18.7	2.6
Group D	31.2	1.1	18.3	2.6
Group E	24.2	1.9	15.3	3.2
Group F	28.3	1.6	15.4	3.2
Group G	28.3	1.1	12.1	3.9
Ordinary after	26.0	1.8	12.0	4.0

2. That practice in reading without articulation can make such reading as good as the ordinary reading of the same individual.
3. That practice in reading without articulation tends to aid ordinary reading, most probably by shortening the habitual practice of articulation.

These experiments cannot answer the question as to whether articulation can be entirely eliminated from the reading process. The amount of practice obtained by the two observers was not sufficient to prevent them from falling back into the habit of articulation. It is questionable whether such a habit, that is of such long standing and so deeply rooted in the adult, can be permanently overcome.

There *seems* to be at least one self-contradiction present within the series of three numbered points listed in the beginning of the above quotation. Point one is that silent speech is unnecessary to the reading process; yet point two seems to imply that it is a *help* to that process. The third point, in turn, seems to contradict the second by asserting that ordinary reading will be improved if silent speech is removed.

What Pintner really means here (and says, also, in the running text preceding his summary) is that reading without articulation, if trained, can be accomplished as effectively as the *long-established, habitual* "ordinary reading," i.e., reading with articulation; and that after a period of reading purposely without articulation, the ordinary reading improves due to the fact that, now, articulation is used less than before the period of training.

Pintner has shown that the process of counting aloud (the element of distraction that he used) becomes automatic during the course of the tests. Yet he does not think that this is the cause of the improved reading values through the trials A-G in Table 2 (pp. 150-151).

The real objections to Pintner's work, however, can be stated as follows:

1. Pintner has neglected to point out that the improvement in ordinary reading, as experienced during the course of the experiment, is due to such factors as the fact that the observers, after the trials with inhibition, are more accustomed to the whole experimental situation.
2. The mere fact that clapping the hands during silent reading had no effect upon the reading values of the observers does not prove that the action of *counting* has no effect on those values either; or that this action has a constant effect of any kind, on the reading values, throughout the experiment. Thus, the increased automaticity may be responsible for the improved reading values.
3. The nature of the results obtained (as reported on in Table 2), using only two subjects, is not such as to justify conclusions as wide as those there drawn by Pintner.

Further, Pintner's main working premise (a premise which is similar to those which have been characteristic for all of the experimenters who have used distraction), viz., that inward articulation can be removed by means of saying aloud some numbers over and over again, also seems highly doubtful.

Clark (1922) made use of the experience of all her predecessors and, in the last of five different experiments, registered simultaneously both laryngeal and tongue movements. She obtains no further results from the four subjects used in this experiment (in all, she used 10 subjects in her various experiments), however, than the familiar, vague notion that although inner speech is of importance to the thought processes, a lot of thinking clearly occurs without it.

Agnes M. Thorson (1925) gives a short résumé of the work of earlier investigators and a criticism of the same. Her criticism may be summarized briefly as follows:

1. Apparatus of the rubber bulb (rubber drum) type used by practically all earlier experimenters for taking recordings of tongue movements is unsatisfactory, since it reacts as well to all other kinds of changes (i.e., than those due to inner speech) in the mouth cavity: swallowings, changes in air pressure due to breathing, and the like.
2. *All* tongue movements have customarily been interpreted as indications of internal speech.
3. The apparatus used has caused discomfort for the subject and directed his attention to the very thing which is to be measured, which might suggest movements. The same objection can therefore be made to the experimental parts as is made to the introspective parts of the earlier experiments. Thorson claims that this seems especially true of Reed's technique.[1]

Thorson's apparatus and the way it works is shown in Fig. 3. In using it, she aimed to test the following (p. 6):

1. Do movements of the tongue occur constantly or with any significant frequency during internal speech?
2. Are the movements which occur identical in their form to those of the corresponding overt speech?
3. If so, are they an essential element of internal speech or only an incidental consequence of it?
4. If they do not occur regularly, what is the significance of the occasional movements which have been reported?

---

[1] Unfortunately, this applies as well (perhaps to an even greater extent) to Thorson's own apparatus.

24

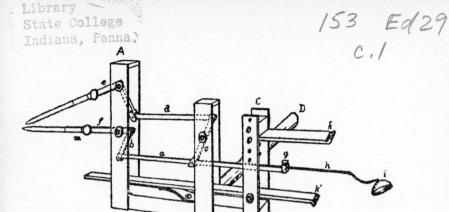

Fig. 3. Thorson's experimental apparatus (x 0.5).

ABC: rigid frame supported in adjustable clamp by the rod, *BD. i:* metal suction cup for attachment to tongue. *a:* aluminum bar, attached to suction cup by the aluminum wire, *h,* adjustable by the set screw, *g,* and transmitting movements through the links and bell-cranks, *b, c, d,* and *e,* to the writing points. The writing points are adjustable horizontally by thumb screws, *m,* acting against light bronze springs.

Table 3. *Pattern of tongue movements during whispering and during internal speech. A comparison made by Thorson (1925, p. 14).*

Subject	Similar		Dissimilar	
	No. of pairs of curves	%	No. of pairs of curves	%
K	2	28.6	5	71.5
D	0	0.0	14	100.0
H	0	0.0	14	100.0
M	0	0.0	12	100.0
L	0	0.0	14	100.0
A	2	15.4	11	84.6
G	0	0.0	16	100.0
N	0	0.0	15	100.0
D	0	0.0	14	100.0
B	2	16.7	10	83.3
Totals	6	4.4	125	95.6

25

Table 4. Pattern of tongue movements during repetition of the same tasks in internal speech. A comparison made by Thorson (1925, p. 14).

Subject	Identical		Similar		Dissimilar	
	No.	%	No. of pairs of curves	%	No. of pairs of curves	%
K	0	0.0	2	28.6	5	71.4
D	0	0.0	1	7.1	13	92.0
B	0	0.0	4	33.3	8	66.6
H	0	0.0	0	0.0	14	100.0
M	0	0.0	2	16.7	10	83.3
D	0	0.0	0	0.0	14	100.0
L	0	0.0	0	0.0	14	100.0
A	0	0.0	2	15.4	11	84.7
G	0	0.0	2	12.5	14	87.5
N	0	0.0	4	26.6	11	73.4
Totals	0	0.0	17	13.0	114	87.0

Table 5. Pattern of tongue movements during repeated whispering of the same tasks. A comparison made by Thorson (1925, p. 16).

Subject	Identical		Similar		Dissimilar	
	No.	%	No. of pairs of curves	%	No. of pairs of curves	%
K	2	28.6	5	71.4	0	0.0
D	2	14.3	10	71.4	2	14.3
B	4	33.3	8	66.6	0	0.0
H	6	42.8	7	50.0	1	7.2
M	3	25.0	9	75.0	0	0.0
D	0	0.0	14	100.0	0	0.0
L	0	0.0	13	93.0	1	7.0
A	2	15.4	5	38.5	6	46.2
G	7	43.8	8	50.0	1	6.2
N	7	46.7	5	33.3	3	20.0
Totals	33	25.2	84	64.2	14	10.6

The experiments were so organized that the subject in question, at each of five different sittings, was given a group of tasks to be performed. The tasks consisted, for example, of mental multiplication, reading of an ordinary text or of "nonsense lines," or of the repeating several times of a line of verse or of meaningless syllables. The tasks were performed, in part, in a whisper, and in part silently.

From the graphic records obtained from these performances, data were calculated partly for a comparison between pattern of tongue movements during whispering with pattern of movements during internal speech (Table 3), and partly for comparisons of how the different subjects reacted when the same phrase was read two different times in internal speech (Table 4). She also gives data from two consecutive recordings where the same tasks were performed, both times in a whisper (Table 5).

On the basis of her experiments, Thorson was able to conclude that tongue movements do not always accompany "internal speech or verbal thought." She maintained further that when they do occur, they correspond very poorly with those movements which accompany similar activity in overt speech. Even upon repetition of the same verbal thoughts, the incidence of similar or identical tongue movements is very small.

Thorson believed her experiments to have shown that tongue movements during mental activity occur more readily after overt speech, under distraction and when the individual in question is working for speed. Emotional disturbance, according to Thorson, had very little effect on the frequency of tongue movements in her experiment; she therefore maintained that the content of the tasks to be performed has less importance for the occurrence of tongue movements than have conditions of "nervous irradiation and muscular tonus." The truth of this last claim seems dubious, and the present author will return to the question at a later point (p. 84, ff.).

The same year as Thorson's report appeared, a similar one was made by Scheck (1925). His method of studying the involuntary movements of the tongue, however, was more similar

27

to Reed's than to Thorson's. A small, toy rubber balloon was the instrument that picked up the occurring tongue movements, while respiratory movements were registered by means of a conventional pneumograph. The signals thus obtained were recorded together on a smoked kymograph drum. Scheck concludes that involuntary tongue movements are very common, if not always present, in accompaniment with thought. Contrary to Thorson, he says that mental stress heightens tongue activity, and that this activity also varies as to rate and amount, depending on the specific stimulus present.

The material which has thus far been presented concerning experiments which were conducted to determine the occurrence or non-occurrence of silent speech in thinking has not included any experiment which has yielded reliable data. The experimental apparatus has in all cases been so primitive that pure artifacts could be the influence behind the experimental results.[1] All the same, it was these experiments which were summarized by Yoakam under a section headed "Vocalization in Reading" in his book *Reading and Study* (1928) in the following assertions (pp. 30-31):

1. The process of vocalization goes on even in silent reading in the case of almost all if not all readers.
2. The amount of vocalization varies with individuals.
3. Lip movements accompany the silent reading of young children and also of inefficient adult readers.
4. It is thought by some that vocalization of a perceptible sort may be unnecessary and could be avoided by the right kind of early training.
5. Vocalization may be decreased by training.

Of these five points, only the first and last appear to require experimental proof.[2] Points two and three can be established from a very superficial examination of a number of individuals. Point four, in the form in which it is made, requires no further support than that supplied by the speculations on the problem made by other authors. As has been indicated above, there is

---

[1] This was pointed out twenty-five years ago by Max (1934).

[2] We say this although there is a slight possibility of ambiguity in Yoakam's use of the word "may" in his fifth statement.

in our opinion no proof for the correctness of point one to be found in the experimental reports on which Yoakam bases his statements. It appears that Yoakam, himself, is aware of this fact, as he presents additional support for point one in the form of the following quotation of W. A. Smith:

That inner speech plays an important part in reading and in thinking generally becomes obvious when once we turn our attention to these processes. And it is quite in accordance with expectation that it should be so. Thinking, speaking and reading are three forms of language activity — each proceeding in terms of symbols of one kind or another, most commonly the word. When we think, we discuss things with ourselves; when we speak we discuss things with others; and when we read we follow the discussion of someone else. In connection with the first two we use the spoken word as a symbol and in connection with the third, the written word.

It must be borne in mind, however, that the written word is a mere transcription of the spoken word and that the two are intimately associated. Moreover, most of us think and speak much more than we read, so that the spoken word is much more firmly imbedded than the written word. It is, therefore, not surprising that the perception of the written word should be accompanied by some degree of articulation and hearing. (Smith, W. A., 1922, *The Reading Process*. New York: Macmillan.)

CHAPTER 2

PREPARATORY EXPERIMENTS BY THE PRESENT AUTHOR EMPLOYING METHODS USED BY EARLIER INVESTIGATORS

Aware of the fact that earlier experimental research on silent speech has been highly limited in its possibilities due, in part, to the primitive recording devices there used, the present writer made experiments which, methodologically, were a continuation of Courten's (1902), Reed's (1916) and Scheck's (1925) work; see pp. 17, 18 ff. and 27-28. The purpose of the present experiments was to see whether or not electrical recording devices with high sensitivity, used together with such mechanical means for carrying off the impulses as those used by earlier experimenters would give more reliable records than had the completely mechanical method of carrying off and recording impulses, as employed by those same earlier investigators. The experiments were concerned with the role played by the tongue, if any, in reading.

Recording Devices and Method

For the direct contact with the tongue, two specially constructed latex condoms were used, one on each side of the tongue. The size and form of the condoms was decided upon on the basis of a series of pilot studies, and the condoms used in the actual experiments were 30 mm. long and 6 mm. in diameter, except at the open end where they narrowed in the form of a neck, making possible direct connections with rubber tubes 3 mm. in diameter. By means of a forked pipe of glass, the tubes from each condom were led to a single rubber tube which, in turn, led to a crystal microphone enclosed in an airtight chamber (Fig. 4). The latex condoms, as well as the tubing connecting them with the microphone, were filled with air. Even upon a very slight mechanical influence upon either of the condoms,

30

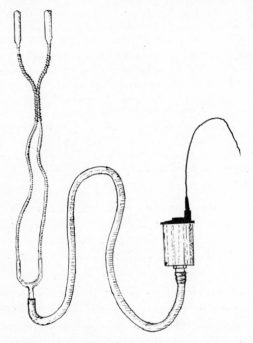

*Fig. 4. Experimental device used by the present author
to pick up impulses from the tongue.*

the pressure caused thereby was immediately transmitted to
the receiving membrane of the microphone. The impulses from
the microphone were then led to a direct-writing recording
instrument, the Elmqvist Mingograf.

The recording system of the Mingograf is as follows. A very fine
jet of liquid is forced from a minute nozzle at high speed. This liquid
jet is directed toward the recording paper which is provided with
a printed graph pattern. The Mingograf has six paper speeds. The
absence of a pen lever or heated stylus, such as are customarily used
in direct writing recorders, limits the inertia of the galvanometer
moving system to the barest minimum. Due to the fact that friction
between the writing lever and the recording paper has also been
eliminated thanks to the jet principle, even very small deflections can
be correctly recorded.

31

The frequency response of the Mingograf is linear to about 500 c/s, although frequencies up to 900 c/s can also be registered. The maximum error of the recorded amplitudes is 0.5 mm for 10 mm deflection at 20 mm length of jet; 1.0 mm for 20 mm deflection at 40 mm length of jet; and 1.5 mm for 30 mm deflection at 60 mm length of jet.

At 40 mm length of jet the maximum sensitivities are better than the following: for the A.C. amplifier, 15 mm/mV; for the D.C. amplifier, 15 mm/100 mV.

The time constant of the A.C. amplifier of the Mingograf is about 2 seconds. The galvanometer has an inner resistance of approx. 0.7 ohm; a deflection of 10 mm at 40 mm length of jet is produced by approx. 125 mA; and the resonant frequency of the galvanometer is approx. 600 c/s.

With the above qualifications, the Mingograf was well equipped to play its part in the accurate recording of even very small changes in the form or in the position of the tongue. It may be added that, of the six paper speeds mentioned above, we used a medium one, viz., 25 mm./sec.

During the experiments with the recording devices described above, considerable difficulty arose in the task of placing the latex condoms correctly. The most satisfactory arrangement was obtained by joining the rubber tubes in the form of a Y by means of a very thin copper wire and of holding in place the part of the Y-stem which remained outside the mouth with a strip of adhesive. The windings of copper wire ran part way up the branches of the Y, as well, and thus it was possible to keep them, and with them the latex condoms, in their proper positions. According to the subjects, the mere presence of the condoms in the mouth did not increase the secretion of saliva perceptibly, nor did it seem to cause any additional tongue movements or swallowings.

Results and Discussion

During the exploratory studies with this recording method, approximately sixty persons, including both adults and school children, were used as subjects. Interpretation of the graphic record was possible in a few cases, but as the successful cases did not constitute more than one in fifteen of the total, the

Fig. 5 a. Record taken from subject X during relaxation.

Fig. 5 b. Record taken from the same subject during
silent recitation.

Fig. 5 c. Record taken from the same subject during reading.

records of those cases were not subjected to statistical treatment, except for a calculation of average deviations from the
zero line of the graph. Average deviations were first calculated
for each of the four most successful cases, individually, for
a section of the graph covering 25 cm., which corresponds to
a recording period of 10 seconds. Single deviations were measured for every tenth of a second (i.e., 100 measurings for each
subject).

The average deviations for the group as a whole during three
types of activity were as follows:

during relaxation: 3 mm;
during silent recitation: 14 mm;
during reading: 12 mm.

For the silent recitation, the subjects said to themselves the
words of the Swedish national anthem, and the reading was of

a passage in French. Fig. 5, a-c, shows records from one of the four subjects whose results could be interpreted.

The fact that the results of these experiments were, as a whole, so discouraging can be attributed to weak points in those parts of the recording system designed to pick up and transport the impulses to the microphone. Irrelevant impulses were caused by changes of air pressure within the mouth exerting pressure on the condoms, slight movements of the condoms or of the transport tubes, and pressure of the subjects' lips on the tubes.

In order to prevent changes of air pressure within the mouth cavity from affecting the recording condoms, and so that only tongue movements give rise to impulses, it would be possible to bind a short tube of plastic, or of some other material, and of greater diameter, between and parallel to the other two tubes, thus providing for immediate equalization of air pressure within and outside the mouth.

If use were made of specially constructed (transport) tubes of flexible plastic or the like, which did not move about so easily as did the rubber transport tubes, it is possible that many irrelevant impulses of the type that enter into the present records might be avoided.

Yet the fact remains that even the smallest movement on the part of the subject, and thus of the tube as well, causes irrelevant microphone impulses which appear on the record quite as the relevant impulses do, rendering interpretation of the latter unreliable or impossible.

Parallel with these experiments, some pilot studies were conducted using a method designed to provide information concerning the electric activity in the speech musculature, viz., the electromyographic method. These pilot studies began to give promising results. If this latter method is compared with the semi-mechanical method described above, the following points are evident:

1. *Concerning the picking up of relevant impulses.* The electrodes used in the electromyographic method, and especially

34

needle electrodes, are easier to keep in place than the latex condoms, thus reducing the occurrence of artifacts due to extraneous movements. The electromyographic method is thus, in this respect, the superior of the two.

2. *Concerning the transportation of the impulses.* In the electromyographic method, fields of electric interference would surely operate on the media of transportation. This element can be counteracted, however, by putting the subject in an electrostatic screening cage. There are, as has been indicated, no totally satisfactory protective measures against distortion during pneumatic transport. The electromyographic method is, therefore, also in this regard, more adequate.

3. *Concerning the registration of the impulses.* In registering the mechanically transported impulses, not more than a fraction of the frequency response of the Mingograf is utilized, as these frequencies are so low. In the registration of the electric impulses, on the other hand, the frequency response of the Mingograf is inadequate, if the individual spike potentials in the record are to be examined; they are not, in this case, however, as only a cumulative record of the bioelectric activity during short periods is desired, without particular respect to the positive and negative spikes. The same registration apparatus can therefore be used in both instances.

To summarize the above discussion, it has not been possible, even with the aid of modern amplifying and registering devices, to improve to any great extent the mechanical experimental methods described in Chapter 1. At this point, it appeared that the best method for obtaining further information concerning the speech motor activities, if any, involved in reading lay in investigation of the electric activity in the speech musculature. A report on the method available for this investigation and on the earlier experiments in this area is made in following chapters.

CHAPTER 3

THE ELECTROMYOGRAPHIC METHOD

Electromyography (EMG) constitutes a relatively recent contribution to medical diagnostic methods. It involves the recording of potentials from active muscles *(action potentials)*. From EMG results, information can be obtained regarding the condition and activity of the muscles concerned. Although this technique is relatively new as a diagnostic aid, its prehistory goes back to the middle of the nineteenth century.

The following review is derived mainly from Lundervold (1951). Galvani's observations of "animal electricity" and his controversy with Volta which resulted from the publication of Galvani's paper in 1791 probably constitute the beginning of the study of the electrical properties of tissues. Although Matteucci, 1838, and Du Bois Reymond, 1843, began to use galvanometers for the measurement of these properties, systematic study of bioelectric currents did not get under way until the early part of the twentieth century. Not until J. Erlanger and H. Gassner, in 1922, used a cathode-ray oscillograph to register these currents, is it possible, with Schaefer in 1940, to speak of "eine ausreichende Physiologie des Aktionsstroms" (a comprehensive physiology of action currents). This method slowly gained a footing in Europe, partly through the work of Rijlant, 1929, and of Schmitz and Shaefer, 1933. Among those who had first investigated action currents in human muscles were Piper, 1907, and Buchanen, 1908; cf., e.g., Piper (1912).

Regarding the physiological mechanisms on which electromyography is based, Buchtal (1957) writes as follows (pp. 9-10):

Whenever a nerve impulse arrives at the region of junction between nerve and muscle the whole of the muscle fibre is thrown into an almost simultaneous contraction. This is brought about by the wave of excitation which moves rapidly along the fibre surface and which stimulates the contractile substance as it passes over the fibre. The stimulus is transmitted along the fibre by an excitable membrane which surrounds the muscle fibre. The action potential results from the break-down of this surface membrane associated with critical changes in ionic permeability. By inserting a minute electrode inside the muscle fibre the potential difference can be measured across the surface membrane and extraneous shunting can be avoided. In the resting muscle fibre the potential difference across the surface membrane is 90 mV, outside positive. During excitation the resting potential is temporarily reversed to 40 mV outside negative. This action potential travels along the muscle fibre at velocities ranging between 3.5 and 5 m per sec. (36.5° C) in different fibres. This variation is small considering that the fibre diameters vary as one to three.

In recording extracellularly, as is done in electromyography, the electrode picks up the action potential as it is conducted through the medium which surrounds the active fibre. The impedance of the external medium is small as compared with the impedance of the fibre interior and hence the voltage of the extracellularly recorded potentials is maximally only two to ten per cent of the intracellularly recorded potential changes. The voltage decreases markedly with increasing distance between active fibre and recording electrode.

Action potentials can be recorded from the muscles either by means of needle electrodes which are placed inside the muscle or by means of surface electrodes applied on the skin.[1] The electrodes are connected to amplifiers and cathode-ray oscilloscopes. In order that the recording of the muscles' action potentials may take place without substantial distortion, it is necessary that the recording devices fulfil the following requirements:

1. a high input impedance, so as to avoid extraneous shunting of the object to be measured;
2. a rather wide frequency range, as not only the basic frequencies are to be measured, but also, to the greatest possible extent, the harmonics.

For the fulfilment of these requirements, Buchtal (op. cit., p. 19) suggests for point 1: 100 megohms, in parallel with 60 $\mu\mu$ F; and for point 2: 2-10,000 c/s.

---

[1] In the work of the present author, both types of electrodes have been used. As the duration and amplitude of action potentials, as well as the number of recruited spikes in the electromyogram, varies according to the type of electrode used, at least in some kinds of muscular activity (Petersén & Kugelberg, 1949), we shall describe the kinds of electrodes used in connection with the report of each particular experiment performed.

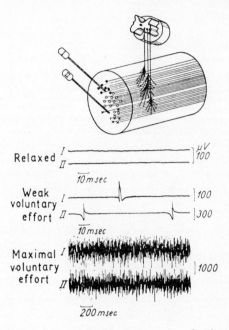

Relaxed $\begin{matrix} I \\ II \end{matrix}$ ————————————— $\left.\begin{matrix} \\ \end{matrix}\right\} \begin{matrix} \mu V \\ 100 \end{matrix}$

$\overline{10\,msec}$

Weak
voluntary $\begin{matrix} I \\ \\ II \end{matrix}$ ———————— $\left.\right\} 100$
effort ———————— $\left.\right\} 300$

$\overline{10\,msec}$

Maximal $\begin{matrix} I \\ \\ II \end{matrix}$
voluntary
effort $\left.\right\} 1000$

$\overline{200\,msec}$

Fig. 6. Differences in electromyograms obtained during
muscular contractions of different strengths
(from Buchtal).

The appearance of an electromyogram varies depending on
the activity of the muscle from which the recording is made.
Even though the muscle action potentials which are recorded
are no direct estimate of the work the muscle is doing, yet
they are clearly related to that work. Several investigators,
e.g., Adrian and Bronk (1929) and Hoeffer and Putnam (1939),
have shown that motor unit[1] potentials increase in number
as well as in frequency when muscular contraction increases.
This relationship is shown in Fig. 6 (taken from Buchtal).
In the case of weak contractions, potentials from a single
motor unit can ordinarily be discriminated (Fig. 7 C). In the

---

[1] A motor unit, as defined in 1925 by Liddell and Sherrington, is "a single
motoneuron, its axon, and the group of muscle fibres innervated by this single
axon."

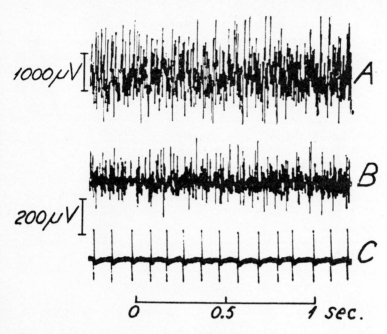

Fig. 7. Different patterns in electromyograms (from Buchtal).

case of strong muscular contractions, the electrode takes up
action potentials from so many different motor units that it
is impossible to distinguish the patterns of single motor units,
and we get an *interference pattern* (Fig. 7 A). Between the
extremes, A and C, there are intermediate forms. If these indicate registrations from a number of different motor units, yet
the potentials of motor units which lie closest to the electrode
can still be distinguished, we speak of *mixed patterns* (Fig. 7 B).
These illustrations thus exemplify the general statement made
above that it is possible by examining the electromyogram to
judge to a certain extent the degree of activity of the muscle.

It should be pointed out that the absence of electric activity
in relaxed muscles has been demonstrated by several investigators: Adrian and Bronk (1929), Smith (1934), Lindsley (1935),
Ingebrigtsen (1938) and Gilson and Mills (1941). Nor have

39

Weddell, Feinstein and Pattle (1944) been able to show electric activity in muscles at rest, and this despite the fact that they used the best known recording and amplifying devices (pp. 181-182):

> If the needle electrode is held immobile or moved slowly and smoothly through a relaxed muscle, no electrical activity is recorded even at the highest amplifications ... once the "insertion" outburst has died away.

It should be noted, however, that it has appeared to a number of investigators that certain muscles cannot be completely relaxed.[1] Weddell et. al. state in this connection (op. cit., p. 189):

> It is possible to relax the majority of voluntary muscles without difficulty. Muscles which cannot be completely relaxed are the neck muscles excluding trapezius, and the intrinsic muscles of the larynx. Among those difficult to relax are the tongue, face and abdominal musculature.

This view is reinforced by Husson (1955) and Fink, Basek and Epanchin (1956) who found electric activity in the speech musculature, even when phonation did not occur, as did Faaborg-Andersen (1957). However, in this regard, see pp. 141-142 of the present work.

As regards the important question whether direct comparisons can be made between electromyograms obtained from different persons, or from the same person on different occasions, the answer is that such comparisons cannot possibly be made, since even electromyograms taken from different places in the same muscle — although the points for picking up the impulses may be located only a few millimeters apart — can be completely different from each other, depending on where the electrode is inserted into the muscle.

The normal range for picking up impulses in electromyographic experiments in which needle electrodes are used is

---

[1] This inability to relax completely should, on the other hand, not be confused with the constant slight tension, the *tone*, which is characteristic of all healthy muscles; this slight tension offers, according to Holmes, 1939, "a steadily maintained resistance to stretching."

40

limited to 1—2 cm. opposite the bevel of the electrode needle. In this connection, Weddell et al. (op. cit., pp. 185-186) state:

It can be shown on theoretical grounds that the action potential of a motor unit can give rise to a recordable impulse for a distance of the order of 4 cm. The discrepancy between this distance and those actually recorded, ¼ to 2 cm., may be explained by the fact that the needle employed has directional properties. ... The rapid diminution of the action potential will be due not so much to distance as to the fibres approaching or crossing the plane at the bevel of the needle.

An additional factor which tends to limit the usability of the method is the fact that a variety of artifacts, such as very slight alterations in contact between electrode and tissue, can be sufficient to cause significant differences in the record. This has caused some authors to suppose that the method in question constitutes no improvement over those methods used earlier for the measuring of muscular activity. Although this seems altogether too strong a criticism, it is important that we remain fully aware of the limitations the method has. Carlsöö (1952) says in this connection (p. 77):

The recording conditions vary. Consequently, no quantitative comparison can be made between one recording occasion and another. The method cannot be used for absolute quantitative registration.

On the other hand, it is possible within the frame of a single experimental occasion to make, on the basis of an electromyogram, relative quantitative comparisons of muscular activity. Carlsöö describes his system for making possible such comparisons as follows (op. cit., p. 77):

... a system of bracketing the registration with a reference activity ... Every test was bracketed with this reference activity, by applying the same load[1] in the first and last registration periods of the observation.

If the same values for activity were indicated on the electromyogram for both of these reference loads, it could be assumed that the recording conditions had remained the same through-

---

[1] This load was thus the independent variable in Carlsöö's experiments.

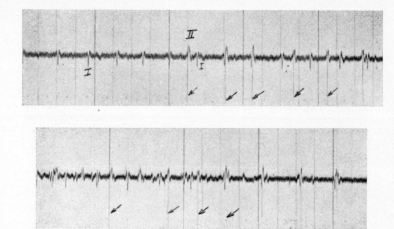

*Fig. 8. Changes in an electromyogram during increasing
contraction of a muscle, according to Wegener.*

out the test. Thus it was possible to make quantitative comparisons concerning the activity recorded within the bracketed periods.

It was clear from the Figures provided earlier in this chapter that action potentials can be observed in greater number as muscle contraction increases. In the case of an electromyogram in which the separate spikes do not come too close to one another, it might seem possible to quantify by calculating peak-to-peak amplitudes. In this regard, however, Inman et al. (1952) state:

> Since the wave form of the muscle action potentials is ordinarily complex, it is inaccurate to simply compare peak-to-peak amplitudes, and it is difficult to make any other comparisons.

In Fig. 8, taken from Wegener (1941), it can be seen clearly that when the contraction increases, motor unit I retains the same amplitude and duration, but a new motor unit (II) becomes active. It is difficult to tell from looking at Fig. 8 whether or not the discharge frequencies for single motor units increase, but as a matter of fact they do.

42

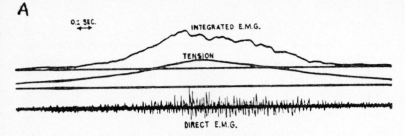

A

*Fig. 9. A direct and an integrated electromyogram
(from Inman et al.).*

This latter fact, as well as the increase in the number of active motor units, when the muscular activity increases, has been demonstrated by Adrian and Bronk (op. cit.) and Hoeffer and Putnam (op. cit.) as was indicated on p. 38, and also by Eccles and Sherrington (1930) and Gilson and Mills (op. cit.). Buchtal (op. cit.) gives these facts the following form in his survey of the electromyographic method (p. 13):

In the muscles of the extremities the single motor units are innervated at a frequency of 5-10 per sec. during weak effort, and of 20-50 per sec. during maximal voluntary effort. A muscle contraction can therefore be graded in part by means of the discharge frequency of the single unit and in part and most importantly by the number of innervated motor units.

In order to be able to study changes in electric activity, Inman et. al. (op. cit.) used an *integrator unit*. This device, which consisted basically of a rectifier, an RC filter network and a balanced amplifier, was used to facilitate measurement of the average amplitude of action potentials. The difference between a directly written electromyogram and an integrator trace is shown in Fig. 9.

In his experimental work, Lippold (1952), in obtaining an integrated electromyogram from ordinary records, also used a special method. Areas enclosed by the electromyogram trace, both above and below the zero line of the electromyogram, were measured by means of a planimeter for a stretch on the electromyogram equivalent to $^{1}/_{6}$ second each. Three such areas from the same recording were selected at random for measurement. A mean area of these three stretches of recording provided the measure of electric activity integrated over a period of $1/_2$ second.

Lippold also, in accord with Buchtal (op. cit.) and other investigators (p. 43), mentions that the changing pattern of the electromyogram, which accompanies changes in muscular activity, is due both to the different number of active motor units and their different discharge frequencies. He also states that the integrated recordings, which it should be noted are a mere transcription of the original ones, are also dependent on these two factors. Thus the integrated recordings are considered to be fully as acceptable as the original electromyogram.

In Lippold's experiment, which involved *isometric contraction*[1] of the gastrocnemius-soleus muscle group of the right leg, he found the existence of a linear relationship between electric activity and muscle tension,[2] with coefficients of correlation ranging from .935 to .995 (n = 30). Lippold therefore concludes (p. 498):

> . . . the recruitment of motor units, bringing about increased strength of contraction, is spatially random. Similarly, there are either random increments of discharge frequencies of the active units, or once a particular unit has become active its rate of contraction smoothly increases.

The very high correlations which have been reported between electric activity in a muscle and the work performed by the

---

[1] *Isometric contraction* (isometric = of equal dimensions) is the term used to refer to the contraction of a muscle which is not allowed to change its length. Isometric contraction is opposed to *isotonic contraction* (isotonic = having a uniform tension). Inman et. al. (op. cit.) and Faaborg-Andersen (1957) have obtained results similar to those of Lippold concerning the relationship between the recorded electric activity and the tension of an isometrically contracting muscle. Carlsöö (op. cit., p. 77) says that if an electromyogram is taken in isometric rather than isotonic contraction, the sources of error in the registration can be considerably reduced.

[2] The muscle tension was measured by means of a dynamometer in which the leg was adjusted in such a manner that measurement was restricted to the work of the gastrocnemius-soleus muscle group.

44

muscle are thus meaningful only in cases of isometric contraction.

In connection with muscle contraction which is not purely isometric, however, there occur within the muscle changes in electric activity which are associated with changes in the number of active motor units and in the discharge frequencies of those motor units. With the aid of an integrator, it is possible to register the total effect of these changes over a certain period of time. This measure can be related to the work done by the muscle in question, to a degree which is sufficient for the purposes of the present work, provided the electric changes which are measured occur during one and the same recording and, among other things, that the electrodes used remain stationary; or, to express the matter in general form, provided the experimental conditions remain constant throughout the recording period concerning which relative quantifications of the electric activity are made.

CHAPTER 4

A DESCRIPTION OF CERTAIN PARTS
OF THE ORGAN OF SPEECH

The Larynx

If any speech movements at all occur in a subject who reads silently, this should be demonstrable in the musculature of the larynx. The larynx alone may not therefore be assumed to be *the* organ of speech. Speech is possible without the larynx, as is exemplified by persons who have developed an esophageal voice after total laryngectomies.[1] However, the larynx is the organ which, under normal circumstances, produces the basic sound which is then transformed into speech sounds by the pharynx, tongue, lips, palate and other parts. The larynx, so to speak, gives out the raw material which determines both fundamental pitch and overtones. These overtones are later modified by the upper respiratory structures.

If we wish to determine whether or not the speech muscu- lature is at work during reading, it becomes clear, even after this brief description, that we must begin by examining that organ which produces the raw material of the sound rather than those which thereafter modify this raw material. It is possible, though not evident, that there occurs during reading a parallelism between the activity, if any, of the intrinsic muscles of the larynx and that of other more easily observed parts of the organ of speech, such as, for example, the tongue. Only after such a parallelism has been demonstrated, can we consider attempting to record silent speech[2] in experimental subjects engaged in reading, from other muscles than the rela- tively inaccessible laryngeal muscles. Attempts to demonstrate

---

[1] Therefore, whenever we use the expression "organ of speech" in the present work we are not referring to the larynx only, but to all parts which contribute to the production of the speech sounds in their final form.

[2] *Silent speech* has earlier been defined (for the purposes of the present work) as "(all instances of) movement in the speech muscles in accompaniment with reading or other forms of mental activity" (p. 14).

such a parallelism were among the earliest in the total series of electromyographic experiments performed by the present author.

Pressman and Kelemen (1955), in their description of the physiology of the larynx, give the following summary of the stages in the production of any given tone, regardless of pitch (p. 546):

1. The cords are adducted to the mid-line and placed under tension by the action of the adductor muscles.
2. Then either the entire length of the cords or varying segments of their more anterior portions, depending upon the tone to be produced, are forcibly pulled apart by the action of those internal fibers of the thyroarytenoidei which insert into and become part of the cords. This is accomplished without any movement whatsoever of the arytenoid cartilages which remain tightly approximated.
3. The hiatus thus produced allows air to escape under pressure which more or less everts the already separated free margins of the cords.
4. The everted cord edges by virtue of their own elasticity spring back into position without in any way affecting the degree of opening established by the pull of the thyroarytenoidei which remains as before.
5. This cycle is rapidly repeated, which repetition represents the vibrations of the vocal cords.

As visible silent speech during reading may be compared to the motor activity involved in whispering, it is quite possible that *less pronounced* degrees of silent speech might constitute similar activity. Therefore the comments of these same authors on whispering are of interest here. The essential difference between whispering and overt speech, they state, lies in the arytenoid cartilages, which function somewhat differently in the two types of utterance. Further (op. cit., p. 546):

In whispering while the arytenoids may undergo the rotary movements familiar to us in speech, the gliding movement upon their facets, which approximates the medial wall of one to that of the other, does not take place.

The result is a wide gap between the posterior parts of the vocal cords, permitting considerable escapage of air. The same authors add (op. cit., pp. 546-547):

The action of the true cords themselves is not greatly unlike that found in speech. In a low volume whisper the cords assume a position a little more closely approximated than that for quiet respiration.

Among the larynx muscles from which recordings might be taken, the most likely are the following: the cricothyroid muscle and the vocal muscle, both of which belong to the adductors, and possibly the posterior cricoarytenoid muscle, the only intrinsic laryngeal muscle which serves as an abductor. In connection with the investigation of possible parallelism between the laryngeal musculature and the rest of the speech musculature, the work of the above named muscles can be recorded simultaneously with that of one of the muscles of the hyoid bone, e.g., the mylohyoid muscle. There follow here brief descriptions of the structure, position, function and innervation of these muscles.

Anatomy and Function of Some Muscles Used in Speech

The following description of certain muscles used in speech is largely according to Brash.[1]

The *cricothyroid muscles* bridge over the cricothyroid interval. Each is partially covered by the thyroid gland and by the sternothyroid and sternohyoid muscles. Between the right and left cricothyroid muscles there is a median triangular area. In this space can be seen the cricothyroid ligament.

The cricothyroid muscle arises from the lateral surface of the arch of the cricoid cartilage. Its fibers which radiate backward and upward are inserted into the inferior border and the adjacent part of the medial surface of the lamina of the thyroid cartilage, and into the anterior border of the inferior horn. The muscle is partly continuous with the inferior constrictor.

The cricoid cartilage is held fixed against the vertebral column by the cricopharyngeus (i.e., the lowest fibers of the inferior constrictor). The action of swallowing, however, constitutes an exception; during this act, the cricoid cartilage is in momentary relaxation. Thus, the thyroid cartilage rotates downward on the cricoid like a visor, when the anterior fibers of the cricothyroid muscle contract; but when we swallow the cricoid rotates on the thyroid. The posterior fibers of the

---

[1] *Cunningham's Text-Book of Anatomy,* ninth edition, 1953, edited by J. C. Brash. London: Oxford University Press (pp. 696-698; 436-437).

48

cricothyroid muscle cause the thyroid cartilage to glide forward. While this action, in certain combinations with other muscles, increases the tension of the vocal folds, its chief function is to make the whole larynx more flexible in movements of the throat.

The *vocal muscle* of each side is a triangular, somewhat prismatic muscle which forms a common muscular mass with the thyroarytenoid muscle. The function and structure of the vocal muscle is still a subject of discussion. Recent research, however, seems to indicate that this muscle consists of a complicated system of fibers arising mainly from the inferior part of the angle between the two laminae of the thyroid cartilage. These fibers run backward to be inserted into the depression on the anterolateral surface of the arytenoid cartilage. There are, in addition, crossed fibers which are inserted directly into the vocal cords.

The vocal muscle produces and adjusts tension throughout the vocal ligament and, aided by the transverse arytenoid muscle in approximating the vocal fold to its fellow of the opposite side, reduces the rima to a mere chink or even closes it altogether.

Each *posterior cricoarytenoid muscle* arises, by a broad origin, from the medial and inferior parts of the depression on the posterior surface of the lamina of the cricoid cartilage at the side of the median ridge. The fibers converge to be inserted into the muscular process of the corresponding arytenoid cartilage. The highest fibers are short and almost horizontal; they are inserted into the back of the muscular process. The intermediate fibers are the longest and are very oblique; they are inserted into the apex of the muscular process. The lowest fibers are almost vertical in their direction and are inserted into the front of the muscular process in common with the lateral cricoarytenoid muscle.

The posterior cricoarytenoid muscle draws the muscular process of the arytenoid cartilage medially and backward and swings the vocal process and the vocal fold laterally. It thereby opens the rima glottidis.

The cricothyroid muscle is innervated by the superior laryngeal nerve, while the other laryngeal muscles described above are innervated by the inferior laryngeal nerve.

The *mylohyoid muscle* arises from the mylohyoid line of the lower jaw to be inserted partly in the lingual process, body, and thyroid cornu of the hyoid bone and partly in a median fibrous raphe extending from the symphysis to the hyoid bone. The left and right mylohyoid muscles meet and form a raphe in which a number of fiber bundles cross over from one side to the other. The mylohyoid muscle, in this way, constitutes the main part of the muscular base of the buccal cavity. It is innervated by the mylohyoid branch of the mandibular nerve.

CHAPTER 5

ELECTROMYOGRAPHIC EXPERIMENTS ON DIFFERENT PARTS OF THE ORGAN OF SPEECH

Earlier Investigations by Other Experimenters and
First Experiments by the Present Author

Recordings from the Larynx

As the present study is concerned not with the activity of a particular muscle or part thereof, but rather with that of a whole group of muscles, viz., those involved in speech, it seemed that the simplest manner of obtaining an electromyogram would be by means of recordings with some kind of surface electrodes. The most obvious first step, then, would be the investigation of possibilities for taking recordings by means of electrodes placed on the throat and close to the larynx. The inner laryngeal muscles would, however, be so effectively screened off, primarily by the thyroid cartilage, that electrodes placed outside the larynx could not possibly be expected to pick up action potentials from these muscles. Therefore, in our experiments with surface electrodes on the throat, we concentrated on attempting to take recordings from the cricothyroid muscle. It appears highly likely, however, that impulses from the nearby sternohyoid and sternothyroid muscles also exercised an influence on the recordings obtained.

It is also clear from an examination of Fig. 10 (from Faaborg-Andersen, op. cit.) that the activity of the cricothyroid muscle both in silent speech and at rest is just above the zero line, i.e., so low that in the graphic record shown, it would be almost impossible to distinguish relevant potentials from the noise of the recording device or from other disturbances. And this is true despite the fact that Faaborg-Andersen conducted his experiments with the aid not of surface electrodes as in our case, but rather with needle electrodes inserted into the muscle in question, which might be expected to produce more de-

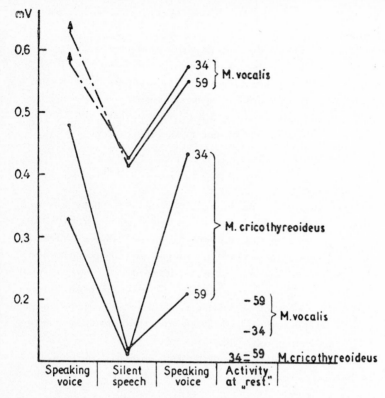

Fig. 10. *Activity in the vocal muscle and in the cricothyroid muscle during phonation, silent speech and relaxation (from Faaborg-Andersen).*

pendable results, as this method both eliminates the possibility of picking up potentials from irrelevant muscles and diminishes the likelihood of extraneous shunting of relevant potentials.

Our possibilities here were thus so small, even at the start, that it is not very surprising that this method proved completely impracticable. Alterations in muscular activity were observed when silent reading was performed after relaxation and after oral reading, but the changes were so small in both cases, the tendency so uncertain and the disturbances so many that we prefer not even to hypothesize regarding the reasons for the changes.[1]

The electrodes used in our experiments consisted of two thin tin disks, each of which was 9 mm. in diameter. In order to hold the disks in position against the muscle, we used tape over the leads to the amplifier as well as over the disks themselves. An electrode paste was used between the disks and the skin in order to minimize resistance in the areas of contact.

Recordings from Other Parts of the Speech Musculature

Attempts to take recordings by means of various kinds of surface electrodes applied on the tongue were made by Kratin (1955). With the aid of the types of contact shown in Fig. 11, he investigated the role of the tongue in the speech process. However, he seems not to have attempted to record silent speech with his apparatus which consisted of one or another of the four types of electrodes used together with an amplifying and registering unit similar to those used in making electroencephalographic diagnoses.

The type of contact which Kratin considered to have given the best recordings was number 4 in the figure, the horseshoe-

---

[1] Birte Binger Kristiansen (1958) is convinced that motor activity occurs in the speech musculature during reading, and states that this fact can be established through the placing of electrodes on the larynx during reading, and then noting the changes in electric activity which occur. She gives, however, no references at all to experimental studies as grounds for her statement. As our investigation showed that no *relevant* recordings can be obtained through the placing of surface electrodes on the larynx, it seems likely that Kristiansen's pronouncement constitutes a supposition that it is possible to do what she says, rather than an assertion supported by facts.

A similar statement appears in Gjessing (1958) who gives Inglis (1948) as his source. Gjessing says that it has been possible with accurate recording devices to demonstrate vibrations of the larynx during silent reading, even in cases of the brightest pupils. In the part of the article by Inglis which is referred to (p. 22), we find only the following: "It is contended as the result of various investigations that most readers use some degree of inner speech in reading. Attenuated movements of the speech organs, such as those that occur in the larynx, are common in mature and efficient readers: readers who use grosser movements, such as those of the lips, are slow and inefficient." For this statement Inglis offers no definite investigations as verification.

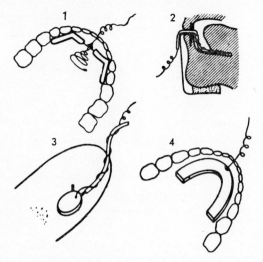

Fig. 11. Different types of electrodes used by Kratin.

shaped electrode which was placed beneath the tongue with the ridge against the gums inside of the lower, front teeth. We, also, have made use of this type of electrode[1] in an attempt to record possible movements of the tongue during reading. It is possible, with high amplification, to obtain fully acceptable registrations with this method,[2] but the number of unsuccessful trials was too great for the method ultimately to be chosen for a study of silent reading. It appears, on the other hand, to be fully satisfactory for investigations of oral reading or of overt speech.

The first experiments in which needle electrodes were used to obtain records of muscle action potentials from the speech

---

[1] A copper bar, 3 mm. wide and 1 mm. thick, was bent into a horseshoe, measuring approx. 2.5 cm. between the tips, and given a silver coating. The lead from the electrode was soldered on to it in the middle of the ridge, and passed between two teeth (as shown in Kratin's figure).

[2] Our best results were obtained, however, not when the other pole was applied to the lobe of the ear (as with Kratin) but when it took the form of a ring of copper wire, insulated on the outer edge, and affixed around a tooth; or of a cannula insulated on the outside except at the tip and inserted into the bottom of the mouth.

musculature were performed by Edmund Jacobson (1956) prior to 1931.[1] The electrodes used in Jacobson's experiments consisted of fine wires of platinum iridium which were inserted through the skin and into the muscle tissue. In the few cases where patients objected to this procedure, surface electrodes were used. The impulses which were picked up were led to a specially constructed string galvanometer. The shadow of the galvanometer wire was magnified 600 times on a screen marked with gradations. The vibrations of the wire were registered by means of continuous photographing of the shadow's movements on the graded white screen. Using this apparatus, Jacobson studied a number of different muscles and muscle groups.

In his experiments on the speech musculature, Jacobson placed the electrodes in the muscles of the tongue or lower lip. The experimental subjects were instructed to imagine counting from one upward, to imagine telling something to a friend, or to think of abstract subjects such as "eternity," "electrical resistance" and "Ohm's law," or of the meaning of the word "incongruous" or "everlasting." Jacobson used subjects who were trained in *differential relaxation*.[2]

In recordings from the muscles of the tongue or lower lip of these subjects, the string galvanometer indicated very nearly no activity at all when relaxation was called for, but as soon as the signal was given for the performance of any of the experimental acts, activity was indicated. If the subjects counted from 1 upward, in one instance speaking as faintly as possible and in another counting completely silently, the registrations from the two instances were very similar in pattern, but with a considerably lower electric activity during the completely

---

[1] The seventh printing of the second edition of Jacobson's *Progressive Relaxation* appeared in 1956, the first edition of the book having appeared in 1929. In the second edition the author summarizes his earlier work, and provides references to his many reports and articles on specific problems published prior to 1938.

[2] By this term, Jacobson means, mainly, the ability consciously to relax individual muscles or groups of muscles. (For a more complete definition, see Jacobson, op. cit., pp. 34, 83.)

silent performance of the task; that is to say, the impulses needed to be considerably more highly amplified in the latter instance in order for the record to be interpretable. Jacobson adds (op. cit., p. 343):

Following each of the objective tests here described, reports were secured in detail from three subjects who had been trained to introspect. They agreed that during mental activities involving words or numbers they feel tenseness in the tongue and lips as in saying those words or numbers, except that the feeling is slighter and more fleeting. These reports conform with our objective findings.[1]

Also of interest in this connection are the experiments performed by Max (1937) during the years 1933-1937 on 18 deaf-mute experimental subjects. Surface-electrode recordings were obtained from muscles of the arms, as "the arms and fingers of deaf-mutes are the locus of their oral, written and gestural speech" (Max, op. cit., p. 302); and comparisons were made with a group of 16 persons with normal speech abilities. The experiment involved the performing of tasks similar to those described by Jacobson above. In 86 percent of the experimental cases studied, muscle activity was observed in the mutes,

---

[1] As regards experimental work on the question of silent speech during other mental activities than reading, it may be of some interest that the present author, in connection with his own experiments in the Stockholm investigation described in a later chapter of this work (p. 110 ff.), completed each individual experiment by having the subject in question, during a direct continuation of the foregoing recording, which in that case was of the electric activity in the mylohyoid muscle, attempt to solve the following problem:

"If any number of six digits in which the same figures appear twice according to the pattern abcabc, e.g., 348348, 176176 or 935935, is divided by 13, the quotient will be an integer. There is a simple principle which proves that this must be true. Try to discover this principle."

The electromyograms which were obtained from that phase of the experiment may be divided into two widely separate categories, one which shows a very great electric activity compared with electric activity during rest for the subjects in question, the other indicating activity approximately the same as that during rest. Provided that the experimental subjects who were responsible for the electromyograms of the latter category thought at all of the task, and provided that pure artifacts, such as discomfort due to increasing secretion of saliva in the mouth, were not the cause of the differences, we are here faced with a very interesting problem. As, however, this does not fall within the main concern of our study, silent speech in reading, we wish in the present connection only to call attention to the above facts.

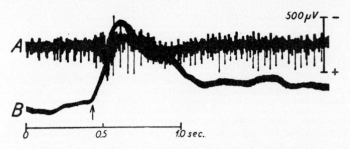

Fig. 12. A record of silent speech, according to Faaborg-Andersen.

A. Action potentials from the vocal muscle.
B. Mean action potential amplitude.
The subjects started to think of saying a vowel at the arrow.

whereas in the control group, on the other hand, such activity occurred only in 31 percent of the cases.

The various investigations described thus far in the present chapter are certainly of value to the present work, yet they are clearly of minor importance for us as compared with the electromyographic study by Faaborg-Andersen (op. cit.) on the functioning of the intrinsic laryngeal muscles in humans. Although the aims of his research were of a nature altogether different from our own, he used in his experiments a method which could be applied, without change, in our work. Faaborg-Andersen's main aim was to study the degree of activity of said intrinsic laryngeal muscles as active in the process of speech, both in the case of healthy persons and in the case of patients with paresis of the vocal cords. However, he has also touched on our problem. Under the heading "Silent Speech," he says in part (op. cit., p. 72):

The amplitude of the action potential pattern was investigated in a series of subjects who were instructed to think about phonation of the vowel "e" without audible phonation. Such a command is often accompanied by movements of the larynx of which the subject himself is not aware.

(See Fig. 12 in the present work.)

56

"Silent speech" was accompanied by an increase in electrical activity and action potential amplitude in both the cricothyroid and the vocal muscles, but the increase was less than during immediately preceding and subsequent audible phonation . . . , markedly less in the cricothyroid muscle.

(See also Fig. 10, p. 51 in the present work.)

The present writer's own basic experimental investigations for the present work were carried out at Faaborg-Andersen's clinic for the treatment of ailments of the ears, nose and throat at the Central Hospital in Nykøbing (Falster), Denmark. We shall, therefore, not report on Faaborg-Andersen's own work at this point beyond the direct quotation above, as relevant details concerning recording apparatus and the like will be given in connection with our own experiments.

Experiments Performed to Establish the Method Later to Be Used in the Main Investigation by the Present Author

Our own electromyographic experiments were performed in two parts, of which the first was conducted in Denmark during the spring of 1958 and the second in Sweden in the late summer and the autumn of the same year. The problems of these two series have been different, as, in part, has been the experimental apparatus. Therefore, the two series will be described separately, the former as the concluding item in Part I, and the latter as the central section in Part II, of the present work.

The Problem in the Denmark Investigation

The fact that an increase in electric activity in the speech musculature occurs during certain types of mental activity had now been conclusively established. The question at this point, therefore, was whether, and if so to what extent, this phenomenon and thus, as well, the silent speech of which it is an indication, might occur specifically during reading. In this connection, it would also be of importance to investigate whether silent speech increased when the reader changed from a less difficult to a more difficult text.

Faaborg-Andersen had obtained his best results concerning silent speech from the vocal muscle. As the placing of electrodes in any part of the inner laryngeal musculature is difficult and associated with certain discomforts for the experimental subjects, we wished to investigate whether we, in other muscles or muscle groups belonging to the organ of speech, could demonstrate, during reading, activity similar to that which had been registered from the vocal muscle. This was all the more desirable since it may be assumed that an experimental situation involving too much discomfort for the subjects might result in their looking through the assigned text without being able really to read it at all properly, which would in turn make the results of the whole experiment doubtful.

Apparatus, Method and Subjects

Included in our earlier brief presentation of the electromyographic method was a statement of the requirements which should be fulfilled by recording apparatus intended for use in electromyographic experiments (see p. 37).

The Disa Electromyograph which was available for use in our experiments in Denmark is constructed wholly in accordance with these requirements. It has three independent electrode-amplifier circuits, permitting simultaneous recording of muscle action potentials from three different points of the same or different muscles. The action potentials, picked up from the muscles by electrodes, are amplified and displayed on cathode-ray tubes placed for observation. The action potentials can at the same time be made audible by a built-in loudspeaker, which can be connected to any of the three amplifier outputs. A continuous film camera employing ten-cm-wide paper is provided to photograph the traces of three additional cathode-ray tubes operating in parallel with those used for observation.

The amplifiers of the Disa Electromyograph employ a special input circuit which permits the action potentials to be recorded without appreciable distortion. The amplifiers have a very low noise level (less than 1.5 μV rms. referred to the input) and a wide frequency range (2-10,000 c/s. defined by 3 db discrimination). Their high input impedance (100 megohms shunted by 50 $\mu\mu$F, measured at the electrode plug box between either of the input leads and ground) and large inphase rejection ratio (greater than 500) permits the taking of electromyograms in almost all locations without screening of the patient, thus eliminating the need for using a shielded room.

Continuous or sweep traces can be recorded on a number of time bases, and with the setting of the time base, the intensity of the cathode-ray spot is automatically adjusted to the proper value for making the recordings.

Of the six time bases available in the electromyograph used, two are intended for continuous recordings where the paper movement serves as the time base, and the remaining four for rapid recordings interrupted at sweep speeds, as follows:

for continuous recording:

a) 20 msec/mm (i.e., a film speed of 5 cm/sec)
b) 5 msec/mm (i.e., a film speed of 20 cm/sec)

for interrupted recording (sweep speeds):

c) 2   msec/mm (which equals a film speed of 50 cm/sec)
d) 1   msec/mm (which equals a film speed of 100 cm/sec)
e) 0.5 msec/mm (which equals a film speed of 200 cm/sec)
f) 0.25 msec/mm (which equals a film speed of 400 cm/sec).

Speeds a) and b) appear, of course, in a continuous photograph lengthwise along the film strip, but c), d), e) and f) are reproduced in a series of separate photographs *across* the continuously moving strip. In our experiments, we used time bases a) and d), the latter in order that we might be able to observe separate action potentials.

For picking up the muscle action potentials a number of different electrodes were used.[1] Thus, for obtaining recordings from the cricothyroid muscle and the mylohyoid muscle, we used a concentric needle electrode (Fig. 13) which consisted of one 0.1 mm. platinum wire lead in the center of an 0.65×42 mm. steel cannula. The platinum wire was insulated from but coaxial with the cannula. The muscle action potentials were picked up between the tip of the platinum wire and the cannula. The tip of the cannula was cut obliquely, the angle being approximately 15°, and the area of the platinum tip was about 0.04 sq. mm. The noise from the electrode surface was 2-4 μV rms. with the electrode inserted in a normal muscle.

---

[1] The medical part of this experiment was conducted by K. Faaborg-Andersen, M.D.

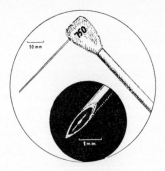 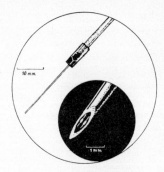

Fig. 13. The concentric　　　　*Fig. 14. The bipolar*
needle electrode.　　　　　　*needle electrode.*

For obtaining recordings from the inner laryngeal muscles we used, on the one hand, an electrode with the same electric properties as the one described above, but in a modified form designed originally for use in the smaller facial muscles. The length of this electrode was thus 25 mm., and the shape of its hilt was identical to that of the bipolar electrode (Fig. 14) which was the other electrode used for recordings from the inner laryngeal muscles. This bipolar electrode consisted of two 0.1 mm. platinum leads insulated from each other and from the 0.65×25 mm. steel cannula. The tip of this cannula was also cut obliquely, the angle being approximately $15°$, providing for a recording area on the tip of each platinum wire of 0.04 sq. mm. The leads spaced approximately 0.2 mm. apart were aligned in the short axis of the cannula tip. Muscle action potentials were picked up between the two tips of the platinum leads, and the noise from the electrode surface here was also 2-4 μV rms. with the electrode inserted in a normal muscle.

In order to keep the electrodes sterilized, we used a Disa electrode sterilizer. It consisted of an electric boiler with, at its base, a series of holes covered with rubber disks. When the distilled water in the boiler was brought to a temperature of $100°$ C., the electrodes were inserted up to the hilt through the rubber disks.

For the purpose of control we required, at the beginning and at the end of each run, the registration of the intoning of audible speech. These registrations were made by means of a crystal microphone with a linear frequency response ranging between 40 and 1,000 c/s. The microphone amplitude was given in mV.

The experimental procedure began with the spraying of the throat or of both the throat and the floor of the buccal cavity of the subject with a solution containing 0.5 percent tetracaine and 0.001 percent adrenalin hydrochloride, so as locally to anaesthetize the pharynx, hypopharynx and laryngeal mucosa, and later, when recordings were desired from the mylohyoid muscle, the floor of the mouth, as well, about the point where the electrode was to be inserted. The subjects were grounded by means of a lead plate which was placed in a wet flannel bag on the back of the neck. The ground connection was improved by putting the flannel bag in a solution of NaCl prior to use.

The ground lead was connected to a plug on the electrode plug box. When the electrodes had been inserted into the muscles from which the recordings were to be taken and the leads fixed in their respective positions by means of adhesive tape attached outside the mouth, the experimental runs were conducted according to the following schedule:

a) intoning of a vowel sound (either [æ] or [ɪː]), repeated five or six times at short intervals
b) total relaxation was requested, about thirthy seconds
c) reading of an easy text in Danish, approx. one minute
d) reading of a difficult text in Danish, approx. one minute
d′) alternative to d), reading of a text in Swedish, approx. one minute
e) intoning of a vowel sound as in a) above.

Items a) and e) were designed to insure that the electrodes were actually in the muscle, making possible the obtaining of a recording, and that they did not move during the course of the run. The recording obtained under b) indicated the "activity at rest" of the muscle in question. The reading of an easy text in Danish, c), and one or the other of the alternatives, d) or d′), the reading of a difficult text in Danish or of a text in Swedish, were of course the central items of the experimental runs.

As we have mentioned earlier, we wished to investigate whether silent speech increased when there was a switch from a less difficult to a more difficult text. Our interpretation of the term *more difficult text* was therefore of fundamental importance. According to the present writer's understanding of the nature of the reading process, a text can be more difficult than a given text if it varies from the latter in one or another or both of two respects. On the one hand, one text can be technically more difficult to read than another, as for example in cases where certain combinations of letters are more difficult to read than others, or where reading is rendered difficult by print which is too small or too large, lines of type which are too long, insufficient spacing between lines, a type face which is difficult to read, or finally, by blurred or otherwise unclear typography. On the other hand, one text can be more difficult than another because of its content. The information provided may be more concentrated. The demand for previous knowledge of the subject may be greater. The mode of presentation may, for reasons connected with the specialized nature of the material presented, be heavy, the choice of words complicated, and so on.

If we wish to deal separately with the first mentioned of the two types of differences in degree of difficulty, we can only do so by the use of meaningless syllables. As we wished, however, to obtain results from a reading situation which was normal so far as the kind of text read was concerned, we chose to render texts more difficult than the given texts mainly according to the latter of these two principles. Therefore, the *criterion of reading ability* also emphasized reading comprehension (Danish Institute of Education Reading Test F III), but it did also take in basic techniques of reading (a modified form of the Danish Institute of Education Reading Test F II, consisting of nonsense words with Danish words mixed in).

After a series of relatively unsuccessful experiments involving simultaneous recordings either from the vocal muscle and the cricothyroid muscle or from the vocal muscle and the tongue (in which series we nevertheless demonstrated relevant activity, during reading, in the muscles involved, and also observed in the cricothyroid muscle an apparent, and in the vocal muscle an obvious increase in this activity when the subject switched from a given to a more difficult text), we arrived at the recording scheme which was then followed during the remainder of the experiment, i.e., combination IV in the listing which follows. The electrode combinations which were tried during these first exploratory series of runs are indicated below. The electromyograph which we used permits recording from three separate electrodes simultaneously. The place from which the recording was taken is given for each of the electrodes that was used.

I. Channel 1: needle electrode in the vocal muscle
   Channel 2: needle electrode in the cricothyroid muscle
   Channel 3: microphone

II. Channel 1: needle electrode in the vocal muscle; in two cases, in the posterior cricoarytenoid muscle instead of in the vocal muscle
   Channel 2: horseshoe-shaped surface electrode[1] beneath the tongue and a ring of copper wire affixed around a tooth
   Channel 3: microphone

III. Channel 1: needle electrode in the vocal muscle
   Channel 2: horseshoe-shaped surface electrode[1] beneath the tongue and a cannula, insulated on the outside except at the tip, inserted into the bottom of the mouth[2]

---

[1] An electrode of the type used by Kratin (see p. 52 and Fig. 11, p. 53).
[2] Attempts were also made as in II.2 above, but with the additional factor that the ring electrode was affixed around the tooth with tape or gutta-percha after the tooth had been thoroughly dried by means of directing upon it a stream of air. This method was possible but took considerably more time than was necessary for III.2.

Channel 3: microphone

IV. Channel 1: needle electrode in the vocal muscle
Channel 2: needle electrode in the mylohyoid muscle
Channel 3: microphone

As the combination used in experiment type IV gave us the clearest and most easily interpreted records, trials were then run according to this method. Both patients and personnel at the hospital, all of whom were Danish, were used as subjects. Particularly when doctors served as subjects, we attempted to follow the course of the run also as it was subjectively experienced, by means of taking notes regarding the introspective analyses of the subjects. These, however, gave nothing of value.

When the electromyographic part of the experiment was completed, the subjects were given the following psychological tests:[1]

1. BPP-56 of the Danish Military Psychological Institute
2. Spelling test of the Danish Military Psychological Institute
3. Reading Test F III of the Danish Institute of Education
4. Modified form of Reading Test F II of the Danish Institute of Education.

Of these, the first test is a conventional intelligence test with very little dependence on verbal factors. The second was used only as a screening test to uncover possible cases of special difficulties in reading and writing; this was impossible to achieve by means of the reading tests which followed, since both of those were tests of silent reading only. The third test examined reading comprehension primarily, and the last was a test of basic techniques of reading with practically no reading comprehension components.

The total experimental time for each subject was two hours and fifteen minutes of which thirty minutes were devoted to the electromyographic investigation.

---

[1] These Danish tests were kindly put at the writer's disposal by the authorities of the Danish Military Psychological Institute and those of the Danish Institute of Education.

64

Results and Discussion

The occurrence of activity in the speech musculature during reading. As has already been stated in a preliminary report (Faaborg-Andersen and Edfeldt, 1958), relevant electric activity was found in the speech musculature of all our subjects during reading as well as during audible intonation. The individual muscles from which the most reliable recordings giving these results were made were the vocal muscle, the posterior cricoarytenoid muscle, the cricothyroid muscle and the mylohyoid muscle. Of these, the nature of the records from the activity of the vocal muscle and the posterior cricoarytenoid muscle indicated that even very small movements in the speech musculature were shown in the recordings from these muscles. This applied almost to the same extent to the records from the mylohyoid muscle. On the other hand the results obtained from the cricothyroid muscle during reading were slight. *The basic question whether or not electric activity, a symptom of muscular activity, occurs in the speech musculature during reading can thus be considered to be answered in the affirmative.* The activity differences can be expressed in millivolts, but since the number of subjects examined was so small (n = 10), we shall not enter into elaborate calculations as proof for the conclusion italicized above, but simply offer an illustrative comparison between the different experimental moments within the recordings obtained from a few of our subjects (Fig. 15—17).

Parallelism between different muscles in the speech musculature. Another question which was considered in the above mentioned preliminary report (Faaborg-Andersen and Edfeldt, op. cit.) was whether there exists a parallelism between different muscles of the speech musculature. This question concerned primarily the relationship between the vocal muscle and the mylohyoid muscle. As indicated in Fig. 15 a, there occur during phonation simultaneous increases in activity in these two muscles. During reading, on the other hand, we can only ascertain that the electric activity in the two muscles reaches maximal values during the same periods of time (Fig. 15 c

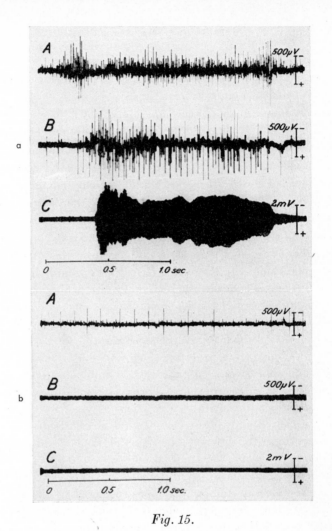

Fig. 15.

and *d*), but at rest there is very little activity in the two muscles (Fig. 15 *b*). This indicates that there exists during reading such a degree of simultaneity in the work of the muscles as to permit us to restrict ourselves to taking recordings from the more easily reached mylohyoid muscle. This is all the more desirable, since recording from the vocal muscle or

66

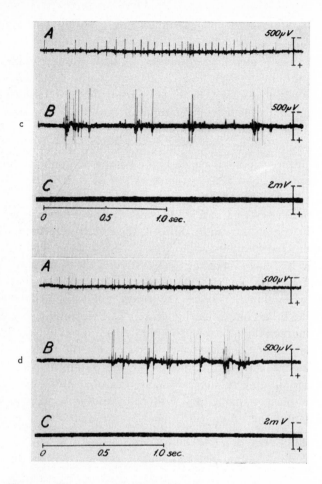

Fig. 15. Electric activity in the vocal and the mylohyoid muscles during reading.

a, b, c and d are from the same subject, a 25-year old medical student with an I.Q. of 140. A: Action potential pattern from the left vocal muscle. B: Action potential pattern from the left mylohyoid muscle. C: Microphone recording.

(a) Phonation of the vowel "e"; frequency 250 c/s. (b) Relaxation during quiet respiration. (c) Silent speech (Danish paragraph). (d) Silent speech (Swedish paragraph).

other intrinsic laryngeal muscles is much more uncomfortable for the subjects.

The degree of difficulty of the text. A comparison of c and d of Fig. 16 indicates that electric activity in the vocal muscle increases when a subject switches from a given text to a more difficult text.[1] If the recording is made instead from the posterior cricoarytenoid muscle, the activity should decline when the switch is made from a given to a more difficult text.[2] As is evident from a comparison of Fig. 17 c and 17 d, this is just what happens. The activity in the latter is clearly less than that in the former. Whether the more difficult text consisted of a Swedish text, as in Fig. 16 and 17, or a Danish text in which the content was more difficult, the results were the same.

A later trial involving comparisons between the reading of a relatively blurred typewritten text and the same text in printed form appeared to give the same result as that indicated for the vocal muscle above: the reading of the blurred text seemed to be accompanied by greater electric activity in the speech musculature.

Reading ability and bioelectric activity. On the basis of the tests which constituted the criterion on reading ability, the experimental subjects were, for purposes of analysis, divided into two groups. One group with poor readers numbered six subjects, and the other, with good readers, four. For each of

---

[1] Regarding what is meant in this connection by the term *more difficult text,* see p. 62.

[2] The reason why we may expect this is that the posterior cricoarytenoid muscle works in opposition to the vocal muscle, as was evident from the descriptions of the actions of these two muscles provided in Chapter 4, p. 49.

$\rightarrow$

Fig. 16. Electric activity in the vocal muscle during reading.

Subject: 69-year old woman with an I.Q. of 95. A: Action potential pattern from the left vocal muscle. B: Microphone recording.

(a) Phonation of the vowel "e"; frequency 300 c/s. (b) Relaxation during quiet respiration. (c) Silent speech (Danish paragraph). (d) Silent speech (Swedish paragraph).

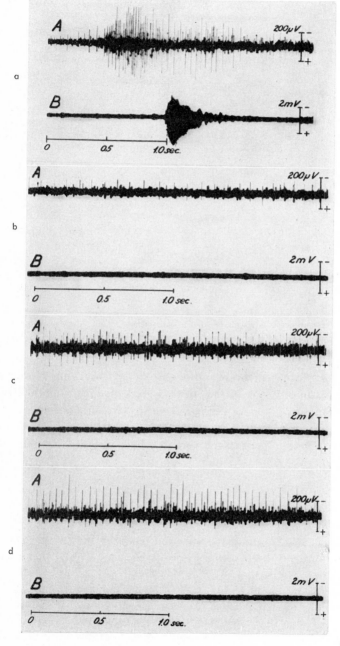

69

Table 6. Reading test results and bioelectric activty in standard scores.

	a Results in the reading tests		b Activity points[1]		
Subject	Test F III	Test F II (modified)	Relaxation	Easy text	Difficult text

Good readers:					
D 5	+1.02	+0.91	—0.57	—0.75	—0.84
D 7	+1.73	+1.12	—0.30	—1.67	—2.12
D 9	+0.86	+1.55	+0.58	—0.44	—0.73
D 10	+1.24	+1.12	+2.66	+1.61	+1.03
Poor readers:					
D 1	—0.94	—0.27	—[2]	—[2]	—[2]
D 2	—0.86	—0.48	—0.74	+0.48	+0.44
D 3	—0.38	—0.80	—0.30	+0.79	+1.19
D 4	—1.18	—0.37	—0.21	—1.16	—0.41
D 6	—1.26	—1.16	—0.83	+0.28	+0.23
D 8	—0.31	—0.91	—0.39	+0.69	+0.98

[1] Recordings taken from the vocal muscle.

[2] This subject is not included in the calculations which follow, as some error has, in his case, affected the electromyographic data.

the ten subjects, the recordings from the vocal muscle during the reading section of the electromyographic investigation, i.e., Danish text + more difficult Danish text, or Danish text + Swedish text, were divided up into periods of 50 milliseconds each. The number of such periods which included a rise in the

⟶

Fig. 17. Electric activity in the posterior cricoarytenoid muscle during reading.

Subject: 46-year old woman with an I. Q. of 95. A: Action potential pattern from the left posterior cricoarytenoid muscle. B: Microphone recording.

(a) Phonation of the vowel "e"; frequency: 425 c/s. (b) Relaxation during quiet respiration. (c) Silent speech (Danish paragraph). (d) Silent speech (Swedish paragraph).

70

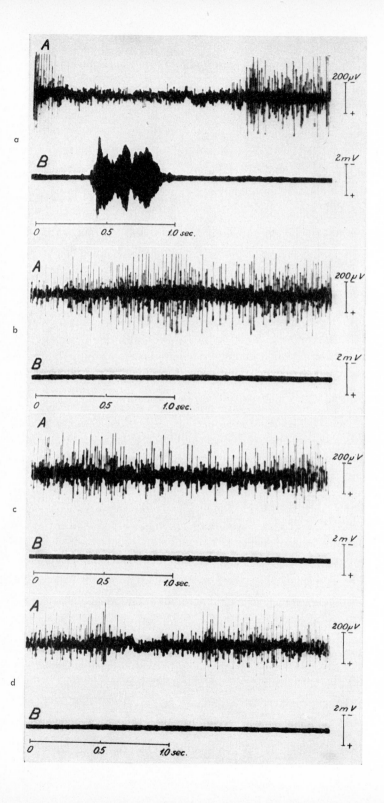

Table 7. Reading points and silent speech points.

	Reading points	Silent speech points
Good readers:		
D 5	+2.95	—0.45
D 7	+4.58	—3.19
D 9	+3.27	—2.33
D 10	+3.60	—2.68
Poor readers:		
D 2	—2.20	+2.40
D 3	—1.56	+2.58
D 4	—2.73	—1.15
D 6	—3.68	+2.17
D 8	—1.53	+2.45

action potentials above the zero line on each electromyogram[1] was then noted. This operation was also performed on the record of action potentials during relaxation. Table 6 gives in standard scores: (a) the results of the reading tests; and (b) the "activity points," i.e., the number of intervals, expressed in percent, in the electromyographic investigation which included an increase in bioelectric activity above the zero line, on the one hand during relaxation, and on the other during reading. None of the subjects examined showed signs of special reading or writing difficulties. (In this latter regard, see p. 64.)

If we take a weighted sum by adding the results under Test F III and Test F II (modified), as shown in Table 6, in the ratio of two to one,[2] we obtain the figures indicated in the left-hand column of Table 7. The percentages for the intervals are, as indicated in Table 6, treated as points for activity (specifically, for frequency of activity), and these *activity points*

---

[1] It should be kept in mind that this zero line is a more or less arbitrary line on each electromyogram, and is not to be confused either with zero electric activity or with electric activity during relaxation. Nor is there any definite relation between the zero lines on the electromyograms for different subjects examined.

[2] We do this because we wish to emphasize reading comprehension in the criterion, as we did in the texts used in the experimental situation (see p. 62).

Table 8. Final experimental results of the Denmark investigation.

Good readers:		Poor readers:	
D 5	+3.40	D 2	—4.60
D 7	+7.77	D 3	—4.14
D 9	+5.60	D 4	—1.58
D 10	+6.28	D 6	—5.85
		D 8	—3.98

for the easy text and the difficult text are added, after which the double of the activity points for relaxation is subtracted from the sum just obtained.[1] The remainders, which may be referred to as *silent speech points,* are given in the right-hand column of Table 7.

If we then add the silent speech points with reversed sign to the reading points, we obtain the figures given in Table 8. That is, we obtain, both for the good readers and for the poor readers, group values which are more separated from each other than are the group values based on reading points only. This appears, on superficial consideration, to constitute a sure basis for the hypothesis that, during reading, poor readers, as one symptom of their poor reading ability, show more electric activity in the vocal muscle than do better readers. This basis is however not provided for by the present material. The small amount of material (10 subjects) which we had at our disposal in this experiment has, as indicated in the above tables, fallen into two relatively clearly defined groups. Among the better readers, three of the subjects had had higher education and one had not. Among the poorer readers, on the other hand, none of the subjects had had higher education. This fact, which from a statistical viewpoint constitutes a serious error in sampling, makes it impossible to interpret the final table at face value. In our main investigation (of students at the University of

---

[1] This is necessary, since the value represented by the relaxation points is assumed to be present both in the values for the easy text and for the difficult one.

Stockholm) on which we report in the second part of the present work, we tested an approximately homogeneous material. In this investigation the problem was as follows:

Null hypothesis: Good and bad readers although of approximately the same age and with approximately the same intelligence and educational background do not differ as regards the occurrence of silent speech during reading.

Alternative hypothesis: There occurs, during reading, less silent speech in good readers than in poor readers, although the readers in question are of approximately the same age and have approximately the same intelligence and educational background.

In both instances here, we mean by silent speech the activity postulated on the basis of the recordings of action potentials in the muscles examined.

In this later investigation, we also examined the influence which the make-up of the text had on the degree of silent speech during reading. The additional independent variables here were the degree of difficulty of comprehension of the text and the degree of clearness of the type.

Silent Speech in Applied Research on Reading and an Experimental Contribution Employing the Electromyographic Method

---

CHAPTER 6

THEORIES CONCERNING THE NATURE OF SILENT SPEECH IN READING

Our concern in Chapter 1 was with the experimental work which has been done on silent speech as a problem of fundamental research. In the present chapter, we shall consider various views and theories on silent speech in its special connection with reading, and more particularly the teaching of reading.

In order to obtain a proper basis for a study of the supposed role of silent speech in reading, we must consider what actually occurs during *reading of any kind*.

In reading, as in conversation, we learn of the thoughts and opinions of another person. The main difference between these two activities is that in reading communication is possible in one direction only. The reader is only informed concerning the opinions of the author. Therefore, in response to the author's presentation, there occurs in the reader, parallel with the reading of the text in question, a kind of inner argument, or else agreement which might take the form of clarification or exemplification. This criticism of the content of a text which is read may be looked upon as one of the most important elements in reading comprehension.

With the invention by the Phoenicians of the kind of writing where the single speech sounds were each represented by a particular symbol or group of symbols (such symbols may be referred to as *letter-sound characters*), the possibilities for expressing in written form that which was spoken were greatly improved. This type of written language was richer in nuances and more mobile than those which had preceded it,[1] but it also required that there be a more exact reproduction in writing of the language which the reader was able to speak. Thus, with this adoption of the use of letter-sound characters, there was lost much of the possibility for communication which had been provided by such earlier techniques of writing as the older Chinese in which the symbols used were the same for very large geographical areas within which the spoken languages were altogether different. The advantage of such a system was that people who could not understand one another's speech could nevertheless communicate with each other in writing.

The above facts indicate to us, as did a similar process of reasoning to W. A. Smith (see p. 29), that reading and speaking have a great deal in common.

There are, as well, indirect indications as to the importance of speech in connection with reading. Investigations such as that of Robinson (1946) show that speech defects seem able to cause specific difficulties in reading and writing. Speech which is free from defects, therefore, provides a desirable base for the teaching of reading. A normal development of sight and hearing is equally desirable. There are also certain minimum intellectual requirements for the individual who is to learn to read; thus, a mental development which is normally found in children of 6 ½ years of age is requisite. This means, among other things, that certain minimum demands are made concerning the child's mass of experience. Included in the latter are, of course, those words which the child uses when speaking or which he understands when he hears them used by others.

---

[1] The earlier types of written languages included, on the one hand, that in which a symbol represented an idea or concept (such symbols are known as *word-concept characters,* or *logographs*), and on the other, that in which a symbol represented the sound or sounds of a certain syllable (such symbols are known as *syllable-sound characters,* or *syllabaries*).

It is not only during the earliest stages of learning to read that the pupil's oral vocabulary has a bearing on reading ability. The fact that reading is dependent on the spoken language finds expression at all stages of reading ability in relatively high correlations between an individual's over-all performance in reading and his accomplishment in vocabulary tests.

When a person learns to read, there surely occur in the organism certain physiological changes. Regarding the nature of these changes, however, we can only make guesses. Therefore, we shall henceforth speak only of the psychological course of the act of learning to read, which is easier to describe.

The Occurrence of Silent Speech

The experimental investigations reported on in the beginning of Part I were attempts to answer the question whether silent speech occurred in *all* people in accompaniment with mental activities. None of these investigations, however, have satisfactorily cleared up this problem. In our own investigation in Denmark, silent speech occurred during reading in *all* the experimental subjects. Despite the small number of subjects (n = 10), it was possible to note different degrees of silent speech. In two cases, it was so evident as to be observed with the naked eye. The other forms of silent speech which occurred in our subjects were so imperceptible that they could only be recorded electromyographically.

A reasonable hypothesis, with which nothing in our experimental data conflicts, is that silent speech in some form always accompanies reading. This hypothesis, however, may not for the present be considered to have been sufficiently tested.

We have already pointed out that different types of silent speech may be noted. Above all, these different categories are distinguished from each other by their varying degrees of obviousness. We note the following stages:

1. Saying or loud whispering of almost every word.
2. Faint whispering of many words.

77

3. Pronounced lip movements but no sound.
4. Faint (or no) lip movements, no sound, but sufficient movements of the tongue to be felt by the fingers under the lower jaw.
5. No sound, no movements of lips or tongue, but movements in the throat perceptible to the fingers if placed on the throat
6. No sound, no movements of lips or tongue or in the throat, directly perceptible to an observer, but movements which can be registered by means of electromyography.

The first five points in the above list agree largely with a list made up by Cole (1947) in connection with her description of the stages in vocalization passed through by a beginner in reading. Cole's five points were supposed to correspond to different degrees of seriousness of the vocalization (vocalization thus being deemed by Cole to be an undesirable practice in reading), and they cover everything from complete pronunciation of every word down to tiny vibrations of the vocal cords.

In Cole's list, point five was worded as follows (p. 29): "No sound, no lip movement, no movement in the throat perceptible to the fingers." This wording, which completely excludes vocalization, is however followed by a statement on the part of Cole that some movements remain during reading, and that these movements can be registered by instruments more sensitive than are the finger tips. As we have had access to apparatus which made it possible to demonstrate that such forms of silent speech really exist, they have been included in our list as a sixth point.

Other authors have also summarized their observations in similar lists for practical pedagogical purposes. This applies, among others, to Dolch (1948). His list is based on the different stages through which a poor reader passes during a period of remedial work. The reader's improvement is described as follows (pp. 112-113):

First, the lips find it impossible to keep up with the reading but the other speech organs still move. Then the tongue ceases to move but movement still goes on in the larynx. The final stage would be for the larynx movements to cease altogether, but there is much debate as to whether this ever happens with many individuals.

For none of the experiments on which we have reported in Part I and in which attempts were made to determine whether silent speech occurs during different kinds of mental activity, were there available recording devices as sensitive as those which are at our disposal in electromyography. Nor has the discussion on silent speech in reading, on which we have reported above, among more modern educational psychologists concerned with the teaching of reading served to increase our knowledge in the matter. The electromyographic results obtained in our investigation in Denmark, however, indicated that *the hypothesis that silent speech occurs during all reading* was worthy of being more thoroughly investigated. This has been done in the Stockholm investigation (p. 110 et seqq.).

Conceivable Causes of Silent Speech

In the preceding section, we have hypothesized the occurrence of silent speech in all reading. On some occasions when stated in the past, e.g., by Watson (1914), this hypothesis stemmed from the idea that silent speech might be a physiologically required factor in the process of reading. There are, however, no experimental indications to this effect. On the contrary, it is obvious that persons suffering from paralysis of the speech muscles may still be capable of thinking and silent reading.

Regarding motor aphasia, Head (1926) reports on a case in which a patient was able to understand much of what he read silently (which fact was demonstrated by his being able to carry out simple printed instructions), although he had lost all power of oral reading. Speech was, in this case, impossible, but this does not mean that silent speech was also impossible, for by its very definition motor aphasia is the inability to speak and to organize the movements of speaking, although there is not actual paresis of the speech organs.

79

Head's example concerns a person who suffered from aphasia after becoming full-grown, i.e., after he had already learned to read. If the injury had affected a person who was just learning to read, it might be supposed that the ability in silent reading might also have been affected. Such an opinion was advanced, among others, also by Kussmaul (1910) who is of the opinion that both the ability to read aloud and the ability to read silently will be damaged, if aphasia sets in while the patient is still obliged to pronounce words in order to understand their meaning.

Silent speech could, of course, be a physiological aspect of the reading process, yet nevertheless unnecessary to that process. It might thus, for example, be an automatism, a more or less superfluous act which forever ran along merely in accompaniment with reading. The truth of this hypothetical explanation must be deemed highly doubtful. It has not been used by any investigator in this field. Above all, it does not agree with what seems to be the wisdom of the body as regards the conserving of energy.

An explanation of the occurrence of silent speech which is not far removed from the above hypothesis is the following. At the elementary levels of reading, most of the work, both at school and at home, is done orally. This connects the printed text stimulus with oral, speech-motor responses to such a degree that very strongly rooted motor habits are formed.

Connections might also be formed between the printed text and an auditory response, the origin of such a connection lying in the fact that children who are learning to read always hear other people's or their own speech while they are looking at the printed text. We may either speak of these auditory elements separately, as did, e.g., Secor (1900), or include them as a part of silent speech. An instance of the latter classification is provided by Huey (op. cit.) who states (p. 120):

For the readers tested ... it seemed that inner speech was a combination of auditory and motor elements, with one or the other predominating according to the reader's habitual mode of imaging.

80

In the present work, the above mentioned auditory elements will be referred to as *inner hearing*.[1] This phenomenon is seldom taken up for special treatment by investigators. It seems that the auditory habits are not considered as significant for the teaching of reading, either elementary or remedial, as are the motor habits.

The theory that silent speech, being a motor habit, comes from earlier experiences of oral reading is supported, among others, by McDade (1937 and 1941), Buswell (1945 and 1947 a), Durrell (1940), Betts (1950) and Gates (1947). Of the authors mentioned, McDade and Buswell provide the most definite support for the theory (see p. 88).

In order to be able to interpret silent speech as a motor habit resulting from training in oral reading, we must view oral reading and silent reading as two different kinds of reading which act inhibitively upon one another. This was the standpoint taken more and more during the last quarter of the nineteenth century and the first quarter of the twentieth by most of the American educational psychologists concerned with the teaching of reading. According to N. Smith (1934), there was a general move from the recitation of the old days and over to an effective type of silent reading, totally emphasizing the content of the paragraphs read. In the beginning, however, the position of oral reading in the American school was very strong. An obvious aim of the apostles of silent reading was therefore to rid the school schedule, to the greatest possible extent, of oral reading. In the writings of N. Smith (op. cit.), Hyatt (1943) and Witty (1949), we find that this aim was maintained so long that, finally in the 1940's, a balance of opinion became customary on this point. One of the main weapons which the advocates of silent reading seem to have used against oral reading was their hypothesis that oral reading gives rise to

---

[1] *Inner hearing* is the most natural term for this phenomenon. It may seem, therefore, that *inner speech* would have been the best term for the phenomenon which we have termed *silent speech*. *Silent speech,* however, is the term which most clearly emphasizes the point that a person is more active when speaking than he is when hearing.

various forms of silent speech which have a detrimental effect on silent reading.

The view that oral reading and silent reading are two mutually counteractive forms of reading can scarcely be considered to be supported by experimental observations. It seems more natural to view them as two forms of the same ability, and investigations concerning the various abilities which are utilized during reading support this view. An example is the study of eye movements during silent reading and oral reading carried out by Anderson and Swanson (1937). These authors obtained fairly high correlations for the ordinary eye movement variables during silent and oral reading, viz., for:

pause duration	.50
fixation frequency	.68
rate of reading	.68
regression frequency	.59.

When Swanson (1937) studied the relationship between word perception in silent and oral reading, he found as high a correlation as .81 between the total number of errors in the two forms. The number of errors in silent reading was registered by means of tachistoscopic exposure of short phrases, the exposure time being too short to allow more than one fixation on each phrase. After the exposure, the reader had to tell the experimenter what he had read. The most frequent type of error here consisted of substitutions which made up 67 percent of the total number of errors. For this type of error only, the correlation between silent and oral reading was .68.

That effective silent readers are also good oral readers, while poor silent readers also achieve poor results in oral reading was also shown by Fairbanks (1937) who worked with word perception, as did Swanson, and by Rogers (1937) who was concerned with reading comprehension. Fairbanks also found substitutions to be the most frequent kind of error at all levels of reading ability. With poor readers, however, the meaning of the text was more likely to be changed as a result of the substitutions than was the case with better readers.

82

Proceeding on the basis of the studies reported on above and from the experiments of Jacobson (op. cit.) and Max (1937) reported on in Part I (p. 54 et seqq. and p. 55), an alternative hypothesis may be formulated to that which states that silent reading and oral reading work against each other. According to such an alternative hypothesis, silent reading and oral reading are nothing but two different forms of the same process. One of these forms is overt, the other implicit. This alternative hypothesis has, as a matter of fact, been formulated by Anderson and Dearborn (1952, p. 160). Nor does the view that silent speech is a motor habit contradict this alternative hypothesis. Even though a motor habit may be formed during the process of learning to read, nevertheless it is not a question of a motor habit which, so to speak, outlives itself. Rather, it is more a matter of the pupil's becoming used to a correct working procedure. The habit arises because the words must be pronounced in order for the reader to understand what he reads. This means that the support given to reading by speech is, to begin with, very great. As the pupil reads with greater and greater assurance, he has less and less need for this detour through silent speech in order to understand the content of the text. If we judge the performance of a reader without taking into consideration his age, how long he has been subjected to reading instruction and similar factors, we may state regarding a beginner in reading that he reads poorly. An individual with such an, absolutely seen, poor reading ability requires extra aids to get the meaning from a text which he sees. Among these aids, speech, either in its ordinary, overt form or in its silent form is the most important. Therefore, it might be supposed that this is also true for persons who are poor readers despite the fact that they have been given instruction in reading over a long period of time. Poor reading ability would then be the cause for the occurrence of silent speech. Dolch (op. cit.) found this to be the case among those pupils whom he had given remedial reading (p. 111):

"The fact is that lip movements are not a cause but are a result of poor reading. If we improve the reading, we can stop the lip movements."

Viewed in this way, silent speech is no longer a motor habit only. Instead, it can be regarded as a natural aid, a working method, used at all levels of reading ability as soon as special difficulties appear in a text, e.g., a complicated sentence structure or unfamiliar words. Most people have probably had the experience of having to go back and reread a paragraph in order to get its real meaning, and have then, without knowing it, used a greater or less degree of silent speech, or even engaged in ordinary oral reading. Anderson and Dearborn (op. cit.) lead up to this idea in their discussion of the causes and effects of silent speech (p. 167):

In reading readily comprehended materials, inner speech may well be at a minimum, but in efforts to get the meaning of printed materials, which the reader finds difficult, he should be free to call on the deeper reservoir of meaning of spoken language. Under some such circumstance, who of us adult readers has not found himself saying the words to himself?

An example which further illustrates this idea is to be found in Kainz (1956; vol. IV, pp. 164-165), where the author discusses the reading of a musical score. One who is unused to reading music is often obliged to sing or whistle the tones in order to comprehend the content of the notes, while for a person who is experienced and skilful in reading musical scores, these aids are unnecessary. The latter individual experiences the content of the score in larger and larger groups of notes, as soon as he sees them. Before he has attained this ability, however, he has passed through an intermediate stage, where he no longer needed to sing or whistle the notes aloud, but where he thought of how they would sound, i.e., where he has had to resort to some sort of inner hearing. The development thus seems to proceed toward the comprehension of larger units at the same time that the need for obvious aids from the senses decreases.

Thorson did not believe that the content of the text had any effects on the tongue movements she recorded; she compared records of tongue movements in normal reading with

84

those taken when the same subjects read texts in Polish. The ratio for the tongue movements during the reading of the text in Polish was 5 percent less than the ratio for reading of the ordinary text. The Polish text, however, was so difficult that the subjects merely skimmed through it, without making any proper attempt to read it (Thorson, op. cit., p. 24). Thorson could have provided a more interesting illumination of the situation, if the effects on the tongue movements of the reading of texts of a more normally increased range of difficulty had been used for comparison.

, It is possible that silent speech not only provides for better reading comprehension in the sense that the verbal meaning of the content of the text in question is made more clear: even the deeper understanding of a text, the entering into a description provided by the author,[1] might require the employment of silent speech. Such, at any rate, appears to be the case as regards inner hearing. Two friends of the present author's claim that while they are reading a report or a novel written by a person they know they can often hear the voice of that person. One of them claims that this gives him a better understanding of professional reports, the other that the entering into the life and spirit of literary works is thus facilitated.

The objection might be made that it may be the deeper entering into the meaning of the text read that causes silent speech and/or inner hearing, rather than the reverse. In this connection, however, we must avoid confusing this deeper entering into or experiencing of a text with the difficulties the subject has in understanding a given text. An example may be drawn from the author's experiences in leading courses in techniques of reading for adult students. When the adults were pressed for time while reading in an SRA Reading Rate Accelerator, lip movements and head movements appeared at lower and lower speeds, as the paragraphs read became less and less interesting. The greater interest which subjects have in a text which really concerns them will surely result in deeper

---

[1] We may also refer to this deeper entering into a text as (deeper) *experiencing of* or *participation in* the text.

participation. In all cases where it was clear that the subjects really were interested in a text, in the above mentioned course work, it turned out that the text dealt with a topic which was very well-known to them. The reason for silent speech not occurring until higher reading speeds were reached might in the above cases have been a result of the fact that the terminology and content of the text were familiar. This fits very well with the view that silent speech does not occur until there is a need for extra aids in, order that the text may be understood. These observations can thus be understood without the degree of participation in the text needing to be taken into consideration.

As regards inner hearing, a parallel to *inner seeing* seems appropriate. If someone in a party tells about a foreign place, the possibilities for participation in the description are, of course, other factors being equal, greater for a listener who has visual memories from that place. If the parallel is correctly drawn, inner hearing must be looked upon as an aid to greater participation in a read text.

Concerning the causes of silent speech, experimental data is still unavailable. Certain theorists of the teaching of reading maintain that silent speech during silent reading is due to effects from basic instruction in oral reading. There is, however, no proof of the correctness of this opinion.

Other investigators have attempted to show that silent speech is a symptom of difficulties in reading, but here again binding proof has not been forthcoming. This latter theory, however, has the advantage of being indirectly supported by the fact that it has been shown that poorly organized eye movements during reading are a symptom of poor reading ability (e.g., Bayle, 1942).

If we then proceed from the hypothesis that silent speech is a symptom of difficulties in reading, we must also expect to find it among good readers when the text becomes too demanding. The correctness of this conclusion has been tested in the Stockholm investigation (see p. 110 et seqq.).

The Effects of Silent Speech

The effects which silent speech may have on reading can be roughly divided into three categories:

1. unfavorable effects
2. uncertain effects
3. favorable effects.

The unfavorable effects are thougt to be mainly those resulting from the most easily observed forms of silent speech, e.g., lip movements which are believed to delay the rate of silent reading so that it decreases to a rate more or less equivalent to that of its oral counterpart. It should be noted, however, that the rates of silent and oral reading are approximately equal throughout the lower grades of elementary school. This is shown in Table 9.

When these two reading values prove to be more or less identical when older students or adults are tested, it may be inferred that something occurs during silent reading which causes a reduction in reading speed corresponding to that which occurs as a result of the pronunciation of words during oral reading. If lip movements have been observed during silent reading in the subjects in question, naturally it has been easy to conclude that the motor element common to both types of reading is responsible for the slow rate of silent reading, as it is for the limited possibilities for speed during oral reading. Among others, McDade (op. cit.), Buswell (op. cit.), Betts (op. cit.) and Bond and Bond (1952) are thoroughly convinced that such is the case, while others, e.g., Durrell (op. cit.), Gates

Table 9. Reading rates (oral and silent reading) of pupils in the Boston University Educational Clinic. Adopted from Durrell (op. cit., p. 143).

Grade	I	II	III	IV	V	VI
Oral reading	45	80	110	135	150	170
Silent reading	45	70	125	156	180	210

(op. cit.) and Harris (1948) support the theory, but less strongly. As recent a handbook as that of Delwyn G. Schubert (1957) also gives very strong support to this theory (p. 72).

McDade goes so far as to say that children who are to taught reading in the ordinary way are unable to achieve silent reading. He explains that *inaudible reading* is a more adequate term for what they achieve. Buswell agrees with McDade here, but suggests the term *noiseless reading*. Buswell also tried to show that "subvocalization," together with failures in perceptual ability, was the cause of discrepancies between the rate of thinking and the rate of reading comprehension found in a group of subjects. Comparisons of the scores in three tests on the rate of thinking and the scores in a rate of reading comprehension test were expressed in terms of sigma differences, and those subjects who showed sizable differences here were controlled with six different perceptual ability tests and a test of the subvocalization tendency. The quotient between the rate of oral reading and the rate of silent reading was used as the measure of subvocalization. Buswell, however, failed to demonstrate the truth of his hypothesis by means of this procedure. An analysis of only one case of his 77 is given in support of the hypothesis.

Bird and Beers (1933), in a specially designed experiment, considerably earlier than Buswell's work, attempted to discover the manner in which silent speech influenced reading ability. These two investigators set up their experiment in explicit opposition to earlier experiments on the problem. Their predecessors had always allowed the difference between the rates of reading orally and silently to constitute the independent variable; this was also the case with Buswell later on. Bird and Beers, however, used either purposely induced or else purposely inhibited silent speech as an independent variable. They had their subjects read two parallel forms of the Chapman-Cook Speed of Reading Test, either form A or B with "maximum inner speech" and the other with "minimum inner speech." "Maximum inner speech" meant that the subjects were to pronounce every word in inner speech, that is with lip and tongue movements (p. 183), while "minimum inner speech" meant that the subjects were to attempt to read entirely without inner speech. The results of the experiment were based on work with two groups of subjects.

In the case of Group I, the reading of form A was to be carried out with inner speech at a maximum, that of form B with inner speech at a minimum. With Group II, the opposite was the case. The values were always poorer when inner speech was at a maximum. The differences between the means for reading with maximum and minimum inner speech were in both cases significant, with $p < .001$. The authors therefore conclude that an increase in inner speech will necessarily be accompanied by a decrease in the rate of reading.

This conclusion is, however, subject to doubt. In the first place, we do not know whether or not this obligatory maximal or minimal inner speech has the same effects as spontaneous forms of the same phenomenon. Further, we do not know whether these obligatory laboratory forms of the phenomenon produce on reading ability effects wholly due to the fact that they constitute a totally new element in the reading situation. Additional light has been thrown on this aspect of the situation by Fryer (1941) in an investigation which, however, did not involve reading.

Fryer had his subjects perform operations in addition either with conscious articulation or with conscious suppression of articulation. The different scores obtained by his subjects indicated that forced articulation had detrimental effects. These effects, however, were rather weak. Conscious suppression of articulation, on the other hand, had a highly detrimental effect on the results. Whereas Fryer found that this latter *impairment* in the addition tests amounted to an average of 66.4 percent, the subjects who suppressed inner speech in Bird and Beers's reading experiment showed an *improvement* of approximately 12.5 percent for Group I and approximately 20.0 percent for Group II. Prior to comparing these experimental results, one would be more likely to suppose that a mental activity such as reading would suffer more, if something additional was brought

89

to the attention of the consciousness (the forcing or suppressing of articulation) than would be the case with a more automatic activity such as the performing of operations in addition.

Fryer's and Bird and Beers's results are, however, to be interpreted in quite another way. Clearly, what happens is not that something new enters into the focus of consciousness, but rather, it seems, that the very process which constitutes the dependent variable (reading in the case of Bird and Beers and adding in the case of Fryer) becomes a more highly self-conscious performance. This assumption is supported by the fact that the action which is ordinarily most automatic, i.e., addition, is the one which here suffers most.

The criticism (p. 89) of Bird and Beers's work is, however, still valid. Their conclusions are invalid due to the fact that they generalized regarding spontaneous forms of silent speech on the basis of results obtained in connection with experimentally induced forms of the phenomenon. There may be possibilities for training maximal silent speech, so that it becomes almost automatic and thus comparable to spontaneous silent speech. On the other hand, so far as the present writer knows, there have thus far been no experiments conducted in which silent speech has, in any satisfactory way, been minimized. Since we cannot know what the reading scores would be if silent speech were really eliminated, it is very difficult to say anything about the real effects of the phenomenon. Betts (op. cit., p. 450), however, has very firmly stated the opposite opinion:

That any observable form of vocalization — such as silent lip movement, whispering, and low vocal utterance — retards the rate of silent reading has been common professional knowledge since the early scientific studies of reading. For example, in 1894 Adelaide M. Abell reported lip movement as contributing to the difference in the accomplishment of good and poor readers. Practice in reading without lip movement has been demonstrated as producing distinct increases in rate of reading.

In order to make such a statement as the above, a rather safe foundation is required. All that Betts actually has is the following (Abell, 1894, p. 285):

A characteristic correlate, in the case of our subjects, of slow reading, is the actual pronunciation or the vivid articulatory imagination of the words read. This device, which may assist in the comprehension of a strange word or of an obscure meaning, is certainly a hindrance when it becomes habitual. The discouragement of a child's tendency to accompany reading by articulation is an evident pedagogical requirement.

Pintner (op. cit.) has quoted the same passage from Abell in support of his own opinion. He adds (p. 139): "...this process of articulation appears more in the light of a hindrance than anything else." We can accept Pintner's and Betts's point of view as an alternative hypothesis to the null hypothesis regarding the effects of silent speech on reading. Yet it does not seem advisable to make this a one-tailed test by omitting the positive alternative hypothesis, viz., that which would indicate that silent speech aids reading comprehension.

Nor would it be wise totally to overlook the possibility that silent speech might have different effects on reading ability on different occasions. Thus, several authors have attempted to explain silent speech as an aid during the early stages of learning to read, but as a hindrance to effective reading if it is maintained in later stages. Harris (op. cit., p. 139) believes that habitual reading with lip movements definitely has a retarding effect, if it continues beyond the third grade, though speech prior to this time, even if it takes the silent form, aids in the learning of reading.

Gates (op. cit.) holds a similar opinion as to the undesirable effects of silent speech later on in school, but says nothing regarding the beneficial effects at early stages. He states his views as follows (pp. 438-439):

In the primary grades pupils are likely to articulate words quite definitely and fully in their silent reading. In the early stages this habit does no harm for the reason that the pupil can articulate words quite as rapidly as he is capable of reading them. The habit, however, may become fixed, and definite, complete articulation of each word may persist. ... In any case, time is taken to produce in some form the motor organization or the sound of the word. A child subject to any of these habits cannot read more rapidly than the speed with

91

which he can articulate. When his silent reading reaches that level, it is likely to remain until the habit of articulating or imaging the word sounds is eliminated.

If silent speech has any effects at all on reading ability, those effects are either favorable or unfavorable. Several attempts have been made to demonstrate experimentally that there are unfavorable effects, e.g., Bird and Beers's (op. cit.) and Buswell's (1951).[1] However, none of these attempts have been successful. There have been, to the knowledge of the present author, no attempts made to determine whether or not silent speech has any favorable effects on reading. However, there are educational psychologists working in the field of the teaching of reading, e.g., Harris (op. cit.), who believe that silent speech aids reading during the earlier grades of elementary school.

Elimination of Silent Speech

Clearly, the decision by anyone working in the field of the teaching of reading regarding whether or not to try to eliminate silent speech is altogether dependent on that person's specific views concerning the effects of silent speech. There is a main dividing line between those, on the one hand, who think of silent speech as being more or less detrimental to reading and therefore try to eliminate it, and those on the other who view the phenomenon simply as a symptom of poor reading, or even as an aid to better comprehension, and who therefore never tackle silent speech itself. Those in the latter group, however, may very well try to make silent speech unnecessary by means of ordinary or remedial reading instruction. Those who do specifically try to eliminate silent speech may, furthermore, be divided into sub-groups, according to the different methods they use.

One of the very first to perform an experiment on the teaching of silent reading was O'Brien (1921). In this experiment, which was conducted in 1919 during the course of 36 consecu-

---

[1] Fryer (op. cit.) might also be included here, though he did not work on silent speech in *reading*.

tive school days in some 20 schools in the state of Illinois in the United States, the children were divided into three experimental groups and one control group. The experimental groups received different types of reading instruction. Two of them were taught in exactly the same way, except that one of the groups was given exercises to eliminate silent speech as much as the children were able, while the other group was given no information whatsoever about silent speech, nor were they given any exercises to remove it. A comparison of the results from these two groups, as groups, does not show any differences. Even if the groups were divided according to school grades, there were still no trends in the results. Thus, it seemed that the mere attempt to remove silent speech did not produce any favorable effects.

McDade (op. cit.) tried to prevent silent speech from occurring at all. His method of instruction, the *non-oral method*, involved silent reading, and silent reading only, from the very first day at school. Oral reading was postponed until later grades. He had the pupils begin with pre-reading conversational exercises including the use of certain easy words and phrases, which then recurred in silent reading exercises. To begin with, this work consisted of naming everyday objects with the aid of word-and-picture dictionaries and cards on which the words in question were written down. Rather soon, however, the pupils were permitted to work with the short phrases referred to above, and even with short sentences. These sentences were not only to consist of simple words, but were also to be meaningfully associated with a motor response on the part of the pupil.

An experiment in the teaching of reading according to McDade's principles was carried out in a Chicago first-grade class in 1935. Toward the end of the school year, by means of a testing program, two other classes were discovered which corresponded in intelligence level to the original experimental class (A). Of these other two classes, one of them (B) had received reading instruction according to an oral method which emphasized phonics and the other (C) had been taught according to a commonly used method of oral reading but in which the use of phonics was not emphasized. The comparison between these three classes was highly in favor of class A:

Class	Average reading score[1]
A	2.65 ± 0.04
B	2.25 ± 0.08
C	2.09 ± 0.04

Class A was also superior to the other two classes as regarded deviations from mental age expectancy, according to McDade's report. These results justified further experiments, and these were also instituted during the 1936-1937 school year in Chicago. These experiments gave additional support to the observations made in the first experimental class.[2]

As is always the case with experiments designed to test different methods, it is also difficult regarding the experiments outlined above to determine what was the real cause of the superior reading ability in the classes which had been taught according to McDade's method. It might have been certain aspects of this method, but it could just as well have been that the teachers in these experimental classes were stimulated by the experiment as such, and therefore achieved better results. The special teaching materials produced by McDade might have been solely responsible for the improvements in the pupils taught by his method, in which case the same improvements would have appeared even if these materials had been used within the framework of other teaching methods.

Buswell (1945) also performed experiments utilizing the non-oral method. These took place in the Chicago Public Schools and were conducted as follows.

Two groups of pupils were matched with regard to the geographical location of the schools and the socio-economic background of the pupils. One of these groups was given non-oral

---

[1] These scores are according to the Metropolitan Primary Reading Test.

[2] All data concerning these experiments appears in the *Annual Report of the Superintendent of Schools for the Year 1937-1938*, published by the Board of Education in Chicago, pages 32-34.

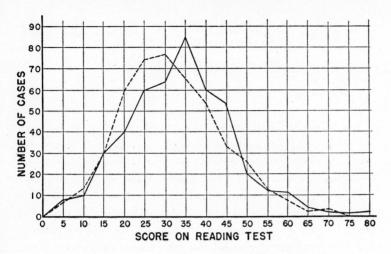

Fig. 18. Buswell's experimental results.

instruction in reading during the first two years of school, while the other group was taught according to conventional methods during the same period of time. The results were not controlled, however, until the pupils had reached the sixth grade, since the interest here was in the more lasting effects of the two methods of instruction used. The 465 pairs of pupils who were tested in the sixth grade with two tests in silent reading were distributed, as regarded their reading scores, in the manner shown in Fig. 18.

The difference between the two distribution means amounts to only 2 points, and the curves are obviously alike. This comparison, thus, does not give support to the statement that the non-oral method of teaching reading produces superior results. Buswell, however, considered the results sufficient ground for making such a statement. Another form of comparison was also made. In approximately half of the thirty-two schools which took part in the investigation, records were made on the pupils who moved their lips or vocalized in some other way, while they were taking the two silent reading tests. The results of this comparison appear in the following table:

95

Group	Number of pupils who were observed	Pupils who showed lip movements, etc.	
		Number	Percent
Oral method	351	75	21
Non-oral method	237	41	17

The non-oral method did not eliminate silent speech any more than did conventional teaching. Yet Buswell states that the superiority of the non-oral method is unquestionable and that this fact is shown by the figures in the above table (1947, p. 525). It must be remembered that the comparison between the two groups was made during the sixth grade. It is possible that if it had been made at the end of the second grade, a higher percentage of pupils from each group would have shown various signs of silent speech. This implies nothing, however, regarding the relationship between the conceivable percentages which might then apply. It only implies the possibility of a decrease in silent speech within both of the two groups, not as a result merely of the methods of teaching used, but as an ordinary development in the reading ability of each individual.

The real objection to Buswell's mode of procedure, however, is as follows. When he wishes to test whether the control group reads less well than the experimental group, he uses as a criterion the occurrence of vocalization. He thus defines a good reader as one without outward signs of vocalization. Such outward signs are lip movements or tongue movements which can be directly seen or felt. Yet he has not first shown that the absence of such signs is a satisfactory criterion of good reading. The comparison of the two groups, based on the results of the objective reading tests, gave such small differences that it is impossible to draw definite conclusions thereupon. It is equally impossible to make any statement concerning the relative values of the methods of instruction used on the basis of the number of vocalizers in the two groups. The only thing Buswell can do here is to investigate whether the non-oral method renders fewer vocalizers than does the conventional method. Beyond that, no conclusions may be drawn.

Both McDade and Buswell thus failed to confirm their basic assumption regarding the superiority of teaching reading by means of the non-oral method.

The teaching of reading by means of the non-oral method appears to be used very rarely today in the elementary schools, which means that most of today's efforts directly designed to remove silent speech in reading are connected with remedial reading.

The educational psychologists who, in their remedial work, proceed on the assumption that silent speech is one of the causes of a low rate of reading comprehension, must naturally try to remove it as much as possible. This applies first of all, of course, to such forms of silent speech as those tongue and lip movements which are outwardly visible. But, on the basis of the above theoretical starting point, even less obvious forms of silent speech, and inner hearing as well, must be eliminated to the greatest possible extent. Among the earliest attempts to produce reading which was completely free from silent speech were Pintner's experiments, reported on in Part I, p. 21 et seqq. Still earlier, Secor (op. cit.) had used a similar method to demonstrate the possibility of purely visual reading. Secor had his subjects recite the alphabet aloud, whistle or sing while they were reading. The experiment was controlled by means of introspection. Since the subjects reported that they were unaware of any tendencies toward silent speech, Secor considered that his experimental method had made it impossible. He used a similar method designed to shut off the auditory elements of inner speech: while the subject was reading, Secor played the xylophone. This, according to the introspective reports of the subjects, eliminated the auditory element which otherwise accompanied reading.

Among Pintner's and Secor's more recent followers, such distractions have been totally discarded, as it has seemed that even very automatic distractions were bound to weaken reading comprehension. In order to hinder lip and tongue movements, much more direct methods have been used. Cole (1938) mentions two different methods for eliminating silent speech, and refers to them as *force* and *intrigue*. Intrigue, the method most reminiscent of the techniques of Secor and Pintner, involved giving to the subjects chewing gum which they were to chew while reading, so that their speech muscles would be prevented from engaging in silent speech. The force method, on the other hand, involves, e.g., requesting the pupil to put two fingers into his mouth. The fingers serve partly to hold down the tongue against the bottom of the mouth and partly to keep the lips and the jaws apart. As an alternative to the fingers, Cole suggests a ruler or a large eraser.

Methods more or less similar to Cole's have been included as an important part in many authors' directions for remedial reading designed to remove silent speech of the lip and tongue movement type. The intrigue method is very strongly advocated by Schubert (op. cit.). Durrell (op. cit., p. 158), on the other hand, prefers the force method, and recommends that the pupils be given a pencil or a paper clip to bite on while they are reading. Gates (op. cit., p. 443) also advocates force methods, though he does not do so altogether wholeheartedly:

To read faster they must try to keep their speech organs inactive; keep the tongue still; not say the words. They should not think of the sounds of the words, but merely look at them, moving along quickly, while trying to get the meaning. In some cases (the teacher) may suggest to the child that he try to keep the tongue still, that he push it hard against the roof of the mouth, compress the lips, or hold the tongue between the teeth. Other devices sometimes tried are putting a clean spoon in the mouth or even a lollypop. In most cases, such devices are not necessary, and in some cases they interfere rather than help.

Bond and Bond (op. cit.) recommend almost the same methods as Gates, but without his pronounced cautiousness, which however is again present in Bond and Tinker (1957) quite as strongly as in the case of Gates. Bond and Tinker also suggest another method which might well be referred to as *the information method*. In direct opposition to the force and intrigue methods, the information method involves informing the pupils regarding the supposed effects of silent speech on their reading.

98

They are then permitted to read relatively simple texts with time limitation, and are supposed to avoid silent speech as much as possible. This same method has been mentioned earlier, incidentally, e.g., in reference to Durrell (op. cit., pp. 159-160) who considered it to be the most important method for eliminating persistent types of inner pronunciation.

When adult reading clinics appeared in the United States, mechanical devices, among others pacers, became very common as aids in remedial reading work. As is usual in such instances, the professionals formed into two camps, those in the one holding the opinion that the pacers were harmful or useless, while the others considered them indispensable. Among the latter, pacers were also used for the elimination of silent speech. Robinson (1953) has collected reports concerning these and similar problems connected with remedial work carried on in classrooms and reading clinics. In several of these reports, pacers are mentioned as useful aids in the effort to remove silent speech.

This applies to an even greater degree as regards authors belonging to that group who work to speed up reading at any cost. The speed-up-your-reading courses given by these reading clinicians to a relatively uncritical public are directed, to a rather large extent, toward the removal of silent speech. In so far as this goal is achieved, the said removal may, in itself, often be used as a proof of the good results of the course. Thus, like Buswell (see p. 96), these reading instructors make the mistake of taking, e.g., the removal of lip movements, as an indication of improvement in reading ability. Yet they, too, have failed to demonstrate first that the absence of lip movements is a sign of good ability in reading.

Errors of this kind are generally present among those who work for the removal of silent speech. Thus, the whole theoretical foundation of this type of remedial reading is weak, and consequently it might even be debated whether it is appropriate to continue with it, as long as its value is so uncertain. Fryer (op. cit.) came to this same opinion, when he discovered that it was impossible to know how mental activity without silent speech would take place and what would characterize it (p. 517):

No method has yet been devised for the study of mental activity where articulation is completely inhibited and no conclusions, therefore, can be drawn as to what actually takes place without articulation. Attempts that have been made to devise methods of learning which inhibit articulation transcend the known facts. All the pedagogical methods in vogue at present to remove articulation in learning should be discarded.

Yet it remains perfectly clear that those pupils who are just learning to read exhibit more, or at any rate more obvious forms of, silent speech than do those persons who have received reading instruction for a longer period of time. In persons whose reading ability is obviously poor, there often appear forms of silent speech similar to those exhibited by beginners in reading. Skilled readers, on the other hand, never seem to be bothered by silent speech of this kind. Some sort of elimination has thus, at any rate, taken place. If this elimination is not a result of attempts directed specifically toward the removal of silent speech, then it seems justifiable to assume that it is connected with the simultaneously observed improvement in reading ability.

Dolch (op. cit.), on the basis of his experiences from remedial reading, believes that what is needed is actual training of the rate of reading on texts which are so easy as to prevent difficulties from arising in connection with the comprehension of the content; during such training, movements of the lips, tongue and larynx will disappear (pp. 112-113):

Usually children lose the habit of sounding simply because they develop such speedy reading that sounding becomes impracticable. First, the lips find it impossible to keep up with the reading but the other speech organs still move. Then the tongue ceases to move but movement still goes on in the larynx. The final stage would be for the larynx movements to cease altogether, but there is much debate as to whether this ever happens with many individuals. But the truth about eliminating lip movements is that, when we read faster than we can speak, we stop pronouncing because we have to.

Judd (1927) reports on a series of experiments the results of which support the theory that the elimination of silent speech

100

takes place during the development of the reading ability. He had five adult subjects count from 1 to 10, from 11 to 20 and from 21 to 30, both aloud and silently, and with time control. When the performances of the subjects were measured in time per series of figures or in the number of figures counted per second, both the quantity and quality of the work of some of his subjects were better, throughout the experiments, when they counted silently than when they did so orally. Others achieved approximately the same results in the two kinds of counting. These latter subjects also had the lowest scores generally.

When the same subjects were asked to read simple newspaper clippings alternatingly aloud and silently, the same tendency was perceivable: the ranking which was set up as a result of the counting tests was valid for the reading tests as well. Judd sees these results against the background of what happens in learning generally. Learning is not to be viewed as an accumulating of fixed neural processes. Rather, it is a process of adjustment in which simpler forms of behavior gradually form into more economic patterns. Thus, it is not so remarkable that during the process of a child's learning to read there occurs a development in which a clear reduction of the amount of vocalization takes place. An apparent absence of vocalization in a person who reads is then a symptom that the individual has reached a point where an internal system of response is more or less totally developed. This system consists of reactions to the content of the text rather than to that of the mere *pronunciation* of the words which the text contains.

Hollingworth's theory of *cue-reduction* might provide additional support to the opinion that the elimination of silent speech is due to the improvement of reading ability. In general, cue-reduction means that while a skill is being refined, several superfluous motions are eliminated. This does not occur as a result of any direct efforts to remove waste motions, but simply because a whole skill is improving. Applied to reading, cue-reduction means, on the motor side, that, e.g., the eye movements become more and more effective. On the sensory side, on the other hand, it means that the reader needs fewer cues from the printed text in order to be able to grasp its content: larger sections of text can thus be taken in in a single fixation. Even if we think of the original pattern of stimulation as a whole, we find that cue-reduction occurs; this means that not only the number of visual cues from the text decreases: the need for auditory and kinesthetic auxiliary stimuli is also considerably reduced.

Anderson and Dearborn (op. cit.) also adhere consistently to this view regarding the elimination of silent speech, and are therefore critical of any type of training specifically aimed at removing it. However, they believe that such training might be useful in connection with interesting a pupil, generally, in improving his reading ability. Beyond this, there are no further aids except large amounts of remedial work on the reading ability as a whole.

The results which then follow from such remedial work are, according to Anderson and Dearborn, more dependent on the qualifications of the pupil than on the teaching method used. This assertion is supported, also, by Buswell's own data, though he sought to demonstrate the opposite (see p. 96). The fact that varying lengths of time are necessary for pupils who are learning reading to dispense with auditory and motor aids might be compared to the fact that some children must use their fingers to help them in counting considerably longer than others who grow out of the habit as early as the first year in school. The above mentioned auditory and motor aids are a common characteristic in the process of learning to read, because responses of recognition to certain objects are already conditioned to the sound of the names of those objects. When a child understands a certain word as a result of uttering the sounds which constitute that word, he does so because the phonemes release this earlier conditioned response of recognition. When this conditioned response is released by the visual stimulus alone, the auxiliary speech stimulus becomes superfluous and is gradually eliminated.

Anderson and Dearborn, then, view the development of reading ability as a part of the total development of the school child. However, this development of the reading ability is not such as to proceed without stimulation from the environment, but like so many other capacities, it too must be trained. If this training is, in certain cases, discontinued too early, or if the methods used for providing it are inadequate, the pupils concerned will be retarded at a lower level of development than in the case of other pupils with the same qualifications. A similar developmental view of reading ability is to be found in Tinker (1952, p. 102):

Transition from vocalizing to thought-getting from visual symbols without vocalization must be learned as any other skill. In normal progress in learning to read under proper guidance there is a gradual transition toward less vocalization so that by the latter part of the third grade the child's silent reading ordinarily is done with little or no lip movements and is faster than oral reading. This transition is necessarily a gradual process.

The following additional facts and observations, though not based on systematic experimentation, may be added. During five years of remedial teaching of adults, the present writer has tried to eliminate silent speech from reading in small groups of students. This never appeared to improve reading ability at all. On the contrary, it seemed that in some cases it may have impaired it. When, however, the remedial work was directed at improving the whole reading ability, without anything being done to remove silent speech, the obvious forms of the latter usually disappeared during the training period. This has been the case even during such short training periods as seven weeks.

Setting of the Hypotheses of the Stockholm Investigation

It is impossible, with our present limited level of knowledge regarding the physiological processes involved in learning generally, to describe what happens when a person learns to read. The changes within the organism which must be assumed to serve as an intermediary variable, e.g., between the quantity of training and the improvement in achievement, constitute

103

a hypothetical construct concerning which we know nothing. The description which follows will therefore be restricted so as to cover only the psychological processes involved in learning to read.

The process in which reading ability normally develops is more or less the same whether the method of instruction used is synthetic or analytic.

When the pupil begins in school, he normally has a vocabulary that has been learned through the kind of conditioning demonstrated in the following diagram.

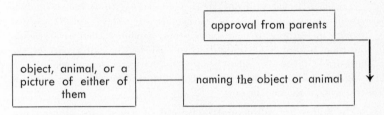

This is in accordance with the scheme:

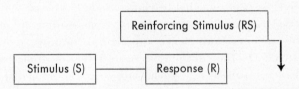

This connection also makes it possible for the child to work the other way and point at a named object or animal. Through increased experience, the recognition of the named object or animal results in a developing understanding of the corresponding concept.

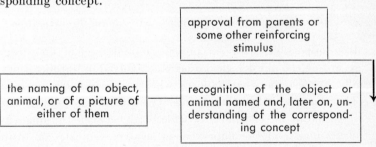

The very naming of an object or an animal constitutes, in learning to read, the unconditioned stimulus in an act of Pavlovian conditioning. Closely connected with this stimulus, and deepening with age and experience, is the understanding of the corresponding concept, which understanding constitutes the unconditioned response. This is true whether the pupil himself names the object or the animal or whether someone else does so.

In the following diagram for Pavlovian conditioning, US indicates the unconditioned stimulus, UR the unconditioned response, CS the conditioned stimulus and CR the conditioned response. The experimental subject is indicated by the letter S.

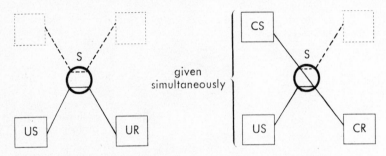

When the teaching of reading is conducted according to the word method, conditioning takes place in the manner indicated in the following diagram.

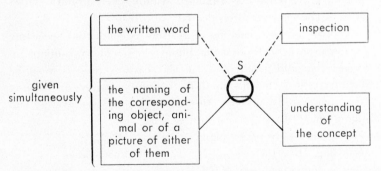

This leads to the next stage, which may be indicated as follows.

105

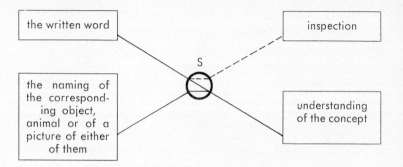

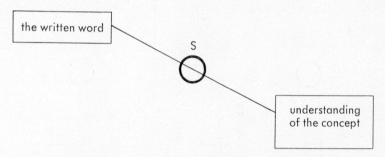

The unconditioned stimulus can be removed after a short period of training, leaving only the following.

The removal of the naming, however, does not imply that all traces of speech are at once eradicated. Silent speech and inner hearing remain as auxiliary stimuli, even after the outer signs of speech have disappeared.

If, however, the teaching of reading is conducted according to a synthetic method using phonics, as is most common in Sweden, an additional phase in the learning process must be included. Since, in this method, reading is based on naming the single sounds correctly, the connection between symbol and sound must first be estab-lished. This also takes place according to the S——R scheme indicated on p. 104. It may be illustrated, by the Swedish vowel »a,» as follows.

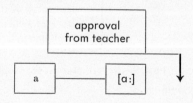

106

When all the sounds have been learned in this manner, the pupil is capable of tackling any word whatsoever. The following conditioning can then take place, if the concept in question is known to the pupil.

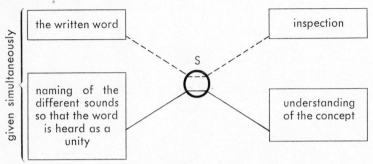

This means that, from the very beginning, understanding of the concept follows directly, if the child correctly sounds up, i.e., names the word.

Since the combinations of symbols, i.e., the words to be drilled, are so numerous, the naming, i.e., the more or less clear pronunciation of a word, remains a relatively long time. Gradually, however, this phase becomes unnecessary, as reading comprehension arises more directly from the visual stimulus of a word, free of the roundabout route through its phonemes. This may be diagramed as follows.

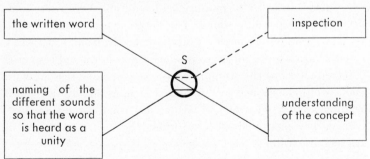

This process of gradual transition to reading without the naming of the sounds or words varies with different pupils, due to their individual qualifications, the intensity of the training

107

and the nature of the textual material used. Nor, of course, does the transition occur once and for all for any of the pupils. In the case of certain easy or well-known words, this transition takes place at a relatively early stage in the process of learning to read. That which then remains of the conditioning scheme is the following.

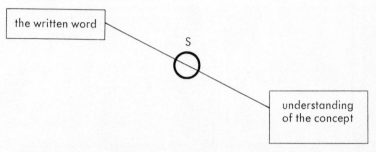

In the case of difficult or unusual words, on the other hand, this transition may never occur. Some kind of naming, or, expressed in the terminology we have adopted, some kind of silent speech may always remain in a person who reads these words.

This does not imply, however, that the original state, regarding word perception, remains, i.e., that, e.g., a child taught according to a synthetic method will always begin the reading of one of these more difficult words by carefully inspecting every letter in order to produce the conditioned response to it, i.e., the corresponding sound. The better a person has learned to read, the fewer single stimuli he needs from a letter, a syllable or a word in order to produce the conditioned response. This reduction of the stimuli necessary to achieve reading with good comprehension is one symptom of more highly developed reading ability. This fact, in so far as visual stimuli are concerned, becomes evident, e.g., when the eye movements of readers are studied.

Another symptom of more advanced reading ability may be that the need for silent speech in any form is reduced almost to nil as regards many of the words which appear in a text. If particularly difficult or unusual words or phrases appear in a text, however, even very good readers resort to the round-about route through naming, i.e., through silent speech, in order to gain a proper grasp of the content of the text.

Silent speech may be placed together with the more generally accepted processes of conditioning which constitute the main part of learning to read. It therefore occurs universally, at any rate so much so that it can be found even in very good readers when they undertake difficult texts. In other categories of readers, silent speech occurs much more often. The phenomenon must therefore be regarded as an aid in, rather than as a hindrance to, reading, and thus every attempt to remove it must be considered objectionable.

From the above discussion concerning silent speech, we can sift out and set the following three hypotheses:

A. Good readers engage in less silent speech than do poor readers.
B. The reading of an easy text results in less silent speech than does the reading of a difficult one.
C. The reading of a clear text results in less silent speech than does the reading of a blurred one.

These three hypotheses were tested in the Stockholm investigation an account of which occupies the remainder of this report.

CHAPTER 7

THE STOCKHOLM INVESTIGATION

As was made clear in our description of the electromyographic method, only relative quantifications of the activity of a muscle can be made on the basis of the measured electric activity in that muscle (cf. p. 41). From the two figures from Buchtal in the beginning of Chapter 3 (pp. 38-39), it was also clear, however, that substantial increases in electric activity occur together with increases in muscular activity. A number of authors (cf. p. 43) report different kinds of changes in electric activity in accompaniment with movements in the muscles. When these electric changes are summated with the aid of an integrator, any increases discovered are connected with an increase in the actual degree of activity of the muscle.

In the experiment by means of which we intended to test our hypotheses, the dependent variable was the electric activity of a muscle expressed in μV, or, in order to avoid too laborious calculations, in the corresponding lengths measured directly on the graphs obtained from the writing unit of our registering device. The independent variables which we wished to test were a person's reading ability (a), and two text variables, viz., the *degree of difficulty of the text as regarded its content* (b), henceforth referred to as the *understandability of the text,* and the *degree of difficulty as regarded technical factors involved in the mere reading of the text* (c), henceforth referred to as the *readability of the text* (see, also, p. 62). Each of these three independent variables though thought of as forming its own continuum, was, for the purposes of the main experiment, divided into distinct groups, as follows:

a, in three groups: a_1: good readers; a_2: medium readers; a_3: poor readers;
b, in two groups: b_1: easy text; b_2: difficult text;
c, in two groups: c_1: clear text; c_2: blurred text.

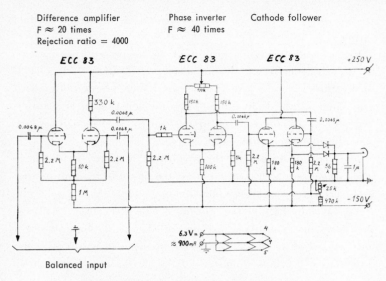

Fig. 19. Diagram of our integrator unit.

Apparatus Used in the Experiment

For the testing of the hypotheses set at the close of Chapter 6, we used a method in some respects different from that described in connection with the report of the Denmark investigation. The main principle was the same, viz., that the values of the dependent variable were to be taken from an electromyogram obtained by means of needle electrodes placed in one of the muscles described earlier (pp. 48-49). For reasons already given, we chose the mylohyoid muscle.

For the picking up of action potentials, we chose concentric needle electrodes, Disa type BK 03, which have been described earlier (pp. 58-59). As, however, we had no reason to be interested in individual spike potentials, but rather wished to obtain integrated values for the electric activity in a muscle during a certain limited period of time, another recording apparatus was used. The impulses obtained from the musculature were led through two different amplifying units before they reached the recording unit, an electrocardiograph of the type described earlier (pp. 31-32).

In the recording apparatus used in the present experiment, the first station which the impulses passed after being picked up by the electrodes consisted of an Elema pre-amplifier with a maximum gain of 30 times. The time constant of this amplifier was 0.1 second and the upper limit of its frequency range was approximately 100 c/s.

The second station of the apparatus may be divided into three stages of which the first consisted of a difference amplifier with a rejection ratio of 4,000 times.

The second stage of the station of which the first stage was the difference amplifier just described was a phase inverter with a gain of 40 times. The phase inverted impulses were fed into the two cathode followers of the third stage. From these, the impulses charged a condenser through diodes. This condenser discharged, through a shunting resistance, with a time constant of 0.3 seconds. If, however, at any point during the course of this discharge, there was an incoming impulse of higher voltage than that of the condenser, the condenser was charged anew with the voltage increment of that impulse. Since we wished to obtain registrations which included even relatively small changes in voltage of the incoming impulses during relatively short periods of reading, we were obliged to choose a rather low time constant. As the time constant becomes lower, the curve becomes less smooth and the interpretation of the records becomes more laborious. A high time constant gives a curve which is free of sharp edges but which, as well, steals a lot of the information which was so badly needed in the present experiment. Approaching maximum information was deemed most important, even though it would give rise to difficulties in interpreting the records; thus, a relatively low time constant was chosen. However, as the discharge of the condenser is an exponential function, it is debatable whether it wouldn't have been better to choose a somewhat longer time constant, e.g., where $\frac{3}{4}$ of the voltage of the condenser would

112

Fig. 20. Picture of all the amplifying units employed.

be discharged within approx. 0.3 sec. In our experiments, however, the time constant used in the second station was 0.3 sec.
Fig. 19 consists of a diagram of this whole station.[1]

From the condenser, the amplified impulses were led to the
third station of the apparatus, which consisted of the Mingograf
the amplifiers and writing units of which have been described
on pp. 31-32. Fig. 20 consists of a picture showing all the ampli-

---

[1] This second station of our apparatus was constructed by Lars Ericsson,
electrical engineer, of the Transmission Branch of the L. M. Ericsson firm in
Stockholm.

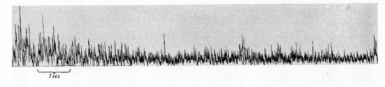

Fig. 21. Recording obtained with our experimental apparatus from the gluteus maximus muscle during decreasing contraction.

fying units employed, and Fig. 21 shows a curve of the kind obtained in the recordings. A picture of the whole experimental apparatus is provided in Fig. 24, p. 119.

The Experimental Subjects

In connection with the reception of new students at the University of Stockholm at the commencement of the 1958-1959 academic year, the present writer gave a series of lectures on the possibilities for bettering a poor ability in reading. Those in the audience who wished to be given a check-up on their reading ability and, possibly, needed advice concerning its improvement signed lists. Of the 600 new students who attended the above lectures, 160 signed the lists, and of these a hundred were chosen at random for participation in the experiment. (The selection of the subjects is discussed at some length on p. 147 ff.) During the preliminary testing, twelve persons were withdrawn, so that for the final electromyographic investigation, there remained 88 persons. Of these, 87, of whom 37 were male and 50 female, participated as subjects throughout the experiment. The results of one of these 87 had to be discarded, due to a temporary defect in the experimental apparatus. In the cases of five persons, the results were somewhat more difficult to interpret, due to the fact that the relevant impulses were recorded on top of a low-frequency oscillation (3 c/s). This was caused by the fact that one of the pre-amplifiers had, accidentally, begun swinging slightly. The defect could not be located before the five subjects had completed the tests. The low fre-

114

quency and regularity in occurrence of the disturbance, however, were such that the values for these subjects did not need to be discarded, but could be used in all cases.

Plan of the Various Parts of the Experiment

The investigation of the students who participated included intelligence testing by means of the F-Test[1] and a determination of reading ability by means of four tests. These latter included three largely conventional type tests, a test in reading speed, a test in reading comprehension and a vocabulary test. A departure from convention, however, was the fact that the reading comprehension test did not involve control by means of multiple-choice type questions, but instead, by means of questions of the open-end type. Of course, this introduced an additional factor of uncertainty in the subjective rating of the degree of completeness of the answers. This factor was, however, countered to the greatest possible extent by means of working out in advance the points to be given for the conceivable variations in the answers. The fourth test designed to contribute toward the determination of reading ability was a Swedish test similar to the Danish Test F II (modified) mentioned earlier (see p. 64). The relationships between these tests, as well as the coefficients of reliability of the tests, are shown in the table which follows.

Table 10. Data concerning the reading tests used.

	Coefficients of reliability	Intercorrelations 2.	3.	4.
1. Reading comprehension test	.72 (split-half)	.36	.38	.19
2. Vocabulary test	.68 (split-half)		.24	.06
3. Speed of reading test	.82 (retest)			.02
4. F II-type test	.90 (retest)			

[1] A thorough description of this test is provided in an unpublished seminar report from the Psychological Laboratory of the University of Stockholm, *Redogörelse för konstruktionsarbete med ett gruppintelligenstest* (A Report on the Work Involved in the Construction of a Group Intelligence Test), 1956.

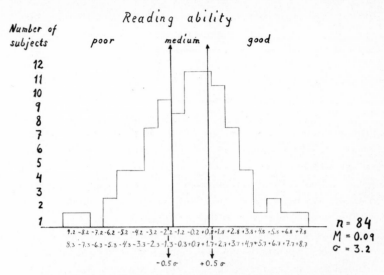

Fig. 22. Distribution of reading results in z-scores and dividing lines between the three reading ability groups.

As the correlations between the tests were so low as to fall between .02 and .38, we considered that there was nothing to prevent us from operationally defining reading ability in our subjects as the sum of the result in the reading comprehension test multiplied by the weight coefficient 2 and the results in the other three tests multiplied by the weight coefficient 1. The reading scores were then transformed into stanine scale values. The manner in which the total reading score was obtained provides for the desired emphasis on reading comprehension in the criterion of reading ability.

When the three sub-groups are formed within the reading ability variable (a), and the understandability variable (b) and the readability variable (c) are dichotomized, the result is that there are theoretically twelve different experimental situations. In the division of the subjects into the sub-groups of variable a,

a_1 good readers

a_2 medium readers

a_3 poor readers,

116

$b_1 c_1$ Samma soliga morgon som Mumin-trollets pappa fick bron över floden
färdig, hittade den lilla Sniff något. Han hittade en mystisk väg. Den
slank in i skogen på ett mörkt ställe, och Sniff stod där länge och tittade
efter den. -Det här ska jag berätta för Mumintrollet i dag, sa han för sig
själv. Vi måste titta på den här vägen tillsammans, för ensam gör jag det
inte. Och så ritade han ett tecken i en tall-stam med sin penn-kniv för att
hitta dit igen. Mumin kommer att bli förvånad, tänkte han och skrattade

$b_1 c_2$ Samma soliga morgon som Mumin-trollets pappa fick bron över floden
färdig, hittade den lilla Sniff något. Han hittade en mystisk väg. Den
slank in i skogen på ett mörkt ställe, och Sniff stod där länge och tittade
efter den. -Det här ska jag berätta för Mumintrollet i dag, sa han för sig
själv. Vi måste titta på den här vägen tillsammans, för ensam gör jag det
inte. Och så ritade han ett tecken i en tall-stam med sin penn-kniv för att
hitta dit igen. Mumin kommer att bli förvånad, tänkte han och skrattade

$b_2 c_1$ Statistiskt äro faktorerna variabler, valda så, att de endast korrelera
med de faktiska variablerna (s.k. orthogonal konstruktion) eller så, att de
därjämte korrelera med varandra (s.k. oblique konstruktion). De ifråga-
varande korrelationskoefficienterna kallas mättnader ("saturations") eller
laddningar (loadings"). Man kan emellertid inlägga olika betydelser i ordet
variabel. I den statistiska facklitteraturen avser man med termen n å g o t,
som kvantitativt varierar.

$b_2 c_2$ Statistiskt äro faktorerna variabler, valda så, att de endast korrelera
med de faktiska variablerna (s.k. orthogonal konstruktion) eller så, att de
därjämte korrelera med varandra (s.k. oblique konstruktion). De ifråga-
varande korrelationskoefficienterna kallas mättnader ("saturations") eller
laddningar ("loadings"). Man kan emellertid inlägga olika betydelser i ordet
variabel. I den statistiska facklitteraturen avser man med termen n å g o t,
som kvantitativt varierar.

*Fig. 23. The opening lines of the four texts used in
reading periods I—IV.*

the total scores from the reading tests, expressed in z-values,
were used as a criterion. Fig. 22 shows the distribution of the
z-scores with the dividing lines for the three groups. Within

117

these groups, there was then performed random distribution, among the subjects, of the four *treatments*[1] that are formed by the possible combinations of variables b and c (b_1c_1 = easy and clear text; b_1c_2 = easy and blurred text; b_2c_1 = difficult and clear text; b_2c_2 = difficult and blurred text; see Fig. 23). When each of these treatments is combined with each of the three reading groups, we obtain the twelve different experimental situations. As we had 86 subjects, it was possible to conduct each of these experiments in seven replicates. Thus, we used 84 of our subjects; the remaining 2 were singled out at random and not used.[2] An experimental design of this type permits the use of a method of calculation which Ostle (1954, p. 350 et seqq.) describes as an analysis of variance for a three-factor factorial in a randomized complete block design, in our case, as mentioned above, with seven replicates.

An attempt was made to concentrate all of the experimental work into the shortest possible period of time. The intelligence tests were thus conducted on October 1 and 3, the reading tests on October 10 and 11 and all of the electromyographic experiments during the week from October 13-18, 1958. The photographing of eye movements was carried out during the period from October 13 to October 27.

The Conduct of the Electromyographic Experiments and Their Results

As the experiments were conducted in an ordinary room at the Institute of Education, some form of shield against electrical disturbances from the lighting system had to be used. For this purpose, a special electrostatically shielded cage of finely meshed chicken-wire netting was constructed. The area of the cage was

---

[1] In accordance with customary practice in analysis of variance, we refer to various combinations of independent variables as *treatments*.

[2] Yet, when calculations were made for reading period II, the records of these two subjects had to be used in order to obtain the 72 subjects there required.

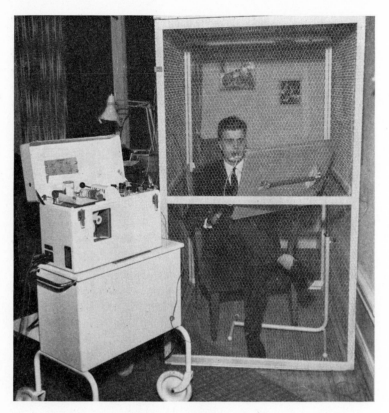

Fig. 24. Over-all view of the experimental equipment.

1 meter $\times$ 1.25 meters and its height, 1.7 meters. The wire
netting was fastened around a wooden frame in such a manner
that there was contact at all points. A contact for ground connection was also soldered directly to the netting. This cage is
pictured in Fig. 24 which also shows the equipping of the inside
of the cage. A chair which was designed to make possible a
comfortable reading situation consisted of an armchair with
a neck-rest, the latter having originally been designed to be
attached to the seat of an automobile. The texts to be read
were placed at a given distance from the subjects on a reading

119

board which was adjusted at a suitable angle. The text was illuminated by a lamp placed outside the cage. The position of the subject during the experiments is also shown in Fig. 24 The ground lead from the cage, together with that from the Mingograf, was connected to the best ground contact in the vicinity from the room in which the experiments were conducted. The ground lead of the subject[1] was connected directly to the chassis of the Mingograf.

When the experimental subject had entered the cage and been informed as to the nature of the experiment, he was given an opportunity to get used to the experimental situation while a few benzocaine lozenges were allowed to dissolve in the mouth at the point where the electrode was to be inserted. The lozenges reduced the sensitivity of the mucous membrane to the injection. When the electrode had been inserted through the base of the buccal cavity and into the mylohyoid muscle, the hilt of the electrode was fixed in position with adhesive plaster outside the mouth.[2] The quality of the recording conditions was checked after which the subject read the texts in an order determined by the following Latin square:

$$
\begin{array}{cccc}
A & D & C & B \\
C & B & D & A \\
D & A & B & C \\
B & C & A & D \\
\end{array}
$$

where: A signified easy and clear text, B signified difficult and clear text, C signified easy and blurred text and D signified difficult and blurred text.

---

[1] The contact here was maintained by means of a metal plate which was spread with a coating of electrode paste and held against the skin by means of a broad, adjustable rubber band.

[2] The placing of the electrodes was handled by Ingemar Bramme, M. B., of Stockholm.

Recordings were made of the first 30 seconds of reading of each text, and between the periods of reading, there were periods of relaxation lasting 30 seconds. Each subject also read a text after a final period of relaxation, and then after an additional period of relaxation, each subject was given a mathematical problem. The complete experimental run for each subject was thus as follows.

1. Electrode control

2. Thirty seconds of relaxation

3. Thirty seconds of reading (reading period I)

4. Thirty seconds of relaxation

5. Thirty seconds of reading (reading period II)

6. Thirty seconds of relaxation

7. Thirty seconds of reading (reading period III)

8. Thirty seconds of relaxation

9. Thirty seconds of reading (reading period IV)

10. Thirty seconds of relaxation

11. Thirty seconds of reading (reading period V)

12. Thirty seconds of relaxation

13. Listening to the experimental leader while he read the mathematical problem

14. Thirty seconds attempting mentally to solve the problem

15. Thirty seconds of relaxation.

The fifth text was included so that the activity observed during the reading of it could serve as a zero point with which the activity during the other periods of reading could be compared. Since the voltage of the measured bioelectric activity is, as mentioned earlier, dependent on the placing of the electrode in relation to the active motor units from which impulses are

121

recorded, the position of the electrode, as well as other recording conditions, must remain constant throughout the period for which comparisons of different measures of activity are to be made; thus, a relative zero point must be established for each subject and experimental occasion. It became apparent, however, that disturbances due to increased secretion of saliva in the buccal cavity rendered the final reading period unsuitable for its intended purpose. The same weakness was, of course, present in the recordings made during the problem-solving phase of the experiment. This has also been dealt with briefly in the footnote on p. 55. In some cases, also, the electrode shifted position, e.g., as a result of swallowing. The comparison of values obtained before and after a movement of the electrode is impossible. Consequently, we chose as a zero point for each subject the activity recorded during a part of the relaxation period immediately preceding the reading periods. As the only measures of activity which were left when the experiments were completed were those to be used in our dependent variable, it was difficult to know when during the total relaxation time the subjects were maximally relaxed. Therefore, our only possibility was to choose as the zero point for each subject a corresponding stretch of a corresponding relaxation period. Thus, we have compared the first to the tenth second of the first reading period with the twenty-first to the thirtieth second of the first relaxation period. The same comparison was made for the recordings from the first to the tenth second of the second reading period. By comparing the average amplitudes of the electromyograms from the relaxation periods before and after each reading period, it was possible to ascertain that the recording conditions had not altered during the reading. Only in one case where the electrode had moved between the first relaxation period and the first reading period, was it necessary to discard the results. In two similar instances where the change was observed in time by the experimenter, the experiment could proceed again from the beginning. The results from an additional seven subjects had to be discarded from the second

secs

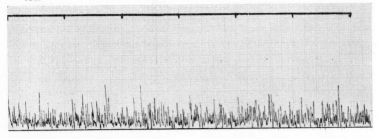

Fig. 25. Specimen of relaxation curve.

Subject no. 71, female, 21 years old; intelligence: under the mean of
the experimental group; reading ability: poor.

secs

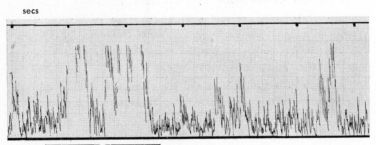

reading with obvious lipmovements

Fig. 26. Specimen of reading activity curve.

Same subject as in Fig. 25.

reading period, as the average relaxation activity before and
after the reading differed in size, indicating that the electrode
had shifted from its original position during the course of the
trial, or that the experimental conditions had altered in some
other way. This might, for example, be because a blood vessel
was struck when the electrode was inserted, the blood then
coagulating during the course of the trial with the result that
the contact conditions at the tip of the electrode were altered.
The values for the third and fourth reading periods have not
been included in our calculations, as they were influenced by

123

disturbances of the kind described above in connection with the extra (fifth) reading period and the problem-solving period.

In order maximally to prevent disturbances which might have influenced the recordings of reading periods I and II from affecting our analyses of these records, we chose to work upon those parts of the respective records which corresponded to the first ten seconds of recording for each period. When we tested the reliability of our registrations (by the split-half method), we found coefficients of correlation as high as .98 for the relaxation periods and .95 for the reading periods. Fig. 25 and 26 show specimens of the records obtained in the Stockholm investigation.

The choice of the short time constant, discussed earlier, for the integrator unit meant that some form of sampling was required before we could proceed with the calculations upon the results for those sections of the records which had been selected for treatment. We decided to measure the height of the curve above the zero-line of the record at every fifth mm. of the curve, which corresponds, in time, to one measurement every 200 milliseconds. This gave us 50 measurements from each relaxation period and the same number from each reading period. When these had been summated for each period separately, the reading activity was expressed in terms of a percentage of the relaxation activity. This value will henceforth, for simplicity's sake, be referred to as the A-quotient (i.e., the activity quotient). The difference in activity between the relaxation period and the reading period was also calculated and will be referred to as the A-difference (i.e., the activity difference). For each subject we also calculated the mean electric activity during the reading period and during the relaxation period, as well as the respective variances for these activities. The significances of the differences between these means were then tested for each subject, as were the respective variances.

There were no significant differences between mean activity in reading and mean activity in relaxation, but the F-tests of the variances gave many significant values. The results of these F-tests are given on p. 125. They are all from reading period I

Table 11. Results of the F-tests made on values from reading period 1.

	Good readers				Medium readers				Poor readers			
	easy		difficult		easy		difficult		easy		difficult	
	clear	blurred	clear	blurred	clear	blurred	clear	blurred	clear	blurred	clear	blurred
	1 5.36 ↗ >.001	2 4.0 ↗ >.001	3 1.25 ↗ =.20	4 6.24 ↗ >.001	5 6.55 ↗ >.001	6 11.15 ↗ >.001	7 1.64 ↗ =.05	8 1.58 ↗ =.05	9 3.26 ↗ >.001	10 5.57 ↗ >.001	11 1.91 ↗ =.01	12 20.95 ↗ >.001
	13 1.02 ↗ <.20	14 1.12 ↙ <.20	15 3.03 ↗ >.001	16 2.25 ↗ .01 <.001	17 8.20 ↗ >.001	18 3.98 ↗ >.001	19 4.38 ↗ >.001	20 4.68 ↗ >.001	21 1.79 ↗ .05 <.01	22 2.98 ↗ >.001	23 4.16 ↗ >.001	24 5,63 ↗ >.001
	25 1.19 ↗ <.20	26 4.37 ↗ >.001	27 2.62 ↗ >.001	28 1.99 ↙ .01 <.001	29 2.21 ↗ .01 <.001	30 1.59 ↗ =.05	31 4.18 ↗ >.001	32 3.81 ↗ >.001	33 12.94 ↗ >.001	34 7.42 ↗ >.001	35 3.01 ↗ >.001	36 12.42 ↗ >.001
	37 1.08 ↗ <.20	38 1.63 ↗ =.05	39 2.15 ↗ .01 <.001	40 1.83 ↙ .05 <.01	41 1.49 ↙ .10 <.05	42 2.60 ↗ >.001	43 3.11 ↗ >.001	44 2.84 ↗ >.001	45 3.12 ↗ >.001	46 1.69 ↗ .05 <.01	47 1.20 ↗ <.20	48 16.39 ↗ >.001
	49 1.04 ↙ <.20	50 2.01 ↗ .01 <.001	51 2.11 ↗ .01 <.001	52 3.78 ↗ >.001	53 2.47 ↗ >.001	54 3.64 ↗ >.001	55 1.62 ↗ .05 <.01	56 5.75 ↗ >.001	57 3.99 ↗ >.001	58 4.31 ↗ >.001	59 2.75 ↗ >.001	60 2.12 ↗ .01 <.001
	61 4.93 ↙ >.001	62 2.02 ↗ .01 <.001	63 1.35 ↗ .20 <.10	64 1.67 ↗ .05 <.01	65 1.73 ↗ .05 <.01	66 5.68 ↗ >.001	67 2.06 ↗ .01 <.001	68 1.07 ↗ <.20	69 4.70 ↗ >.001	70 2.17 ↗ .01 <.001	71 13.79 ↗ >.001	72 3.49 ↗ >.001
	73 1.06 ↗ <.20	74 1.25 ↗ =.20	75 1.57 ↙ .10 <.05	76 2.44 ↗ =.001	77 2.36 ↗ .01 <.001	78 2.83 ↗ >.001	79 10.92 ↗ >.001	80 17.64 ↗ >.001	81 8.76 ↗ >.001	82 3.74 ↗ >.001	83 1.32 ↗ .20 <.10	84 6.33 ↗ >.001

and from the relaxation period preceding it. The data given for each of the 84 subjects is as follows.

A: the experimental subject's number
B: the F-value
C: ↘ the variance of the activity in reading is higher
   ↗ the variance of the activity in relaxation is higher
D: the p-value

As is seen from Table 11, the variances for the reading period are always higher than the variances for the relaxation period among the poor readers; for these poor readers, the p-values are predominantly below the .001 level. This tendency applies, to a large extent, also to the medium readers but weakens greatly among the good readers. See, also, the following summary table.

Table 12. Summary of the results appearing in Table 11.

Category	$p<.001$		$p<\frac{.01}{.001}$		$p<\frac{.05}{.01}$		$p<\frac{.10}{.05}$		$p<\frac{.20}{.10}$		$p>.20$		Σ
	↗	↘	↗	↘	↗	↘	↗	↘	↗	↘	↗	↘	
Poor readers	—	21	—	3	—	2	—	—	—	1	—	1	28
Medium readers ...	—	18	—	3	—	5	1	—	—	—	—	1	28
Good readers	1	7	1	6	1	2	1	—	—	3	2	4	28

↘ the reading activity has the highest σ^2-value.
↗ the relaxation activity has the highest σ^2-value.

If we accept the .01 level as significant, the above table can be broken down so that cases where the σ^2-values for reading activity are significantly higher than those for relaxation activity are separated from those cases where they are not.

126

Table 13. Same data as in Table 12, but arranged for χ^2-test.

Category	σ^2-values for reading activity significantly higher	Other cases	Σ
Poor readers	24 (19.3)	4 (8.7)	28
Medium readers	21 (19.3)	7 (8.7)	28
Good readers	13 (19.3)	15 (8.7)	28
Σ	58	26	84

A χ^2-test of this table gives $\chi^2 = 10.7831$, which in turn gives a p-value of $< \genfrac{}{}{0pt}{}{.01}{.001}$ with 2 d.f. From this it follows that the variability in bioelectric activity within the values for individual subjects is significantly different in the different reading ability categories, it being lowest among the good readers and highest among the poor ones. The same tendency can be seen in the values from reading period II.

The testing of our main hypotheses, however, was by means of the analysis of variance method mentioned earlier. Calculations were made, both on the A-quotients and the A-differences, from the records of the first reading period. Regarding the A-quotients, it was deemed advisable to make calculations on a square root transformation of the values also, since a check by means of Bartlett's test of homogeneity of variance gave a χ^2-value which was relatively high, though not significantly so. This check was made despite the fact that the discussion in textbooks regarding Bartlett's test seems to indicate a doubt regarding its suitability for this purpose. From reading period II, however, only the original A-quotients and A-differences were used as bases for calculations.

There follow here tables with raw scores (A-quotients and A-differences) and results of all five analyses of variance, which were conducted, Tables 14-16 being based on reading period I and Tables 17-18 on reading period II; Table 19 is a summarization of the results of the analyses of variance.

Table 14. Analysis of variance on A-quotients from reading period I.

	a$_1$				a$_2$				a$_3$		
b$_1$		b$_2$		b$_1$		b$_2$		b$_1$		b$_2$	
c$_1$	c$_2$	c$_1$	c$_2$	c$_1$	c$_2$	c$_1$	c$_2$	c$_1$	c$_2$	c$_1$	c$_2$
109	114	114	130	125	177	139	119	161	193	126	251
96	105	141	131	132	199	124	139	147	188	194	199
112	136	114	95	112	155	168	142	174	174	175	194
98	120	126	116	123	129	166	125	135	132	144	303
95	76	117	130	111	125	115	145	190	144	163	162
71	132	101	140	110	112	126	145	156	134	214	180
123	141	80	123	143	179	219	220	184	214	147	188

Source of variance	Sum of squares	Df	Mean square	F	p
Replications	7907.3	6	1317.9	1.714	$<\begin{smallmatrix}.20\\.10\end{smallmatrix}$
a: Reading ability	56642.9	2	28321.5	36.829	$<.001$
b: Understandability of the text	4343.0	1	4343.0	5.648	$<\begin{smallmatrix}.05\\.01\end{smallmatrix}$
c: Readability of the text	6448.7	1	6448.7	8.386	$<\begin{smallmatrix}.01\\.001\end{smallmatrix}$
Interactions:					
a × b	696.1	2	348.1	0.453	$>.20$
a × c	543.6	2	271.8	0.353	$>.20$
b × c	0.8	1	0.8	0.001	$>.20$
a × b × c	5012.8	2	2506.4	3.259	$<\begin{smallmatrix}.05\\.01\end{smallmatrix}$
Exper. error	50756.4	66	769.0		
Total	132351.6	83			

(Total, calculated directly: 132351.8)

Table 15. Analysis of variance on A-differences from reading period I.

a_1				a_2				a_3			
b_1		b_2		b_1		b_2		b_1		b_2	
c_1	c_2	c_1	c_2	c_1	c_2	c_1	c_2	c_1	c_2	c_1	c_2
98	102	107	131	114	301	154	146	390	224	138	268
81	96	163	169	137	225	167	165	217	264	265	355
114	151	127	62	117	253	163	209	224	223	352	258
78	134	170	144	118	199	202	133	168	141	225	352
77	0	116	227	102	164	115	229	321	238	258	285
15	160	91	216	118	114	165	187	310	182	478	198
141	211	33	144	185	271	362	331	259	372	274	251

Source of variance	Sum of squares	Df	Mean square	F	p
Replications	32516	6	5419.3	1.27	$>.20$
a: Reading ability	306723	2	153361.5	35.87	$<.001$
b: Understandability of the text	16464	1	16464.0	3.85	$=.05$
c: Readability of the text	11340	1	11340.0	2.65	$<\begin{matrix}.20\\.10\end{matrix}$
Interactions:					
a × b	366	2	183.0	0.04	$>.20$
a × c	19388	2	9694.0	2.27	$=.10$
b × c	1116	1	1116.0	0.26	$>.20$
a × b × c	12049	2	6024.5	1.41	$>.20$
Exper. error	282145	66	4274.9		
Total	682107	83			

(Total, calculated directly: 682109)

Table 16. Analysis of variance on square root transformations of the A-quotients from reading period I.

| a_1 | | | | a_2 | | | | a_3 | | | |
| b_1 | | b_2 | | b_1 | | b_2 | | b_1 | | b_2 | |
c_1	c_2	c_1	c_2	c_1	c_2	c_1	c_2	c_1	c_2	c_1	c_2
10.44	10.68	10.68	11.40	11.18	13.30	11.79	10.91	13.08	13.82	11.23	15.84
9.80	10.25	11.87	11.45	11.49	14.11	11.14	11.79	12.12	13.71	13.93	14.11
10.58	11.66	10.68	9.75	10.58	12.45	12.96	11.92	13.19	13.19	13.23	13.93
9.90	10.95	11.23	10.77	11.09	11.36	12.88	11.18	11.62	11.49	12.00	17.41
9.75	8.72	10.82	11.40	10.54	11.18	10.72	12.04	13.78	12.00	12.77	12.73
8.43	11.49	10.05	11.83	10.49	10.58	11.23	12.04	12.49	11.58	14.63	13.42
11.09	11.87	8.94	11.09	11.96	13.38	14.80	14.83	13.57	14.63	12.12	13.71

Source of variance	Sum of squares	Df	Mean square	F	p
Replications	13.62	6	2.27	1.94	$< {.10 \atop .05}$
a: Reading ability	97.64	2	48.82	41.73	$<.001$
b: Understandability of the text	7.15	1	7.15	6.11	$< {.05 \atop .01}$
c: Readability of the text	10.55	1	10.55	9.02	$< {.01 \atop .001}$
Interactions:					
a × b	0	2	0	0	—
a × c	0	2	0	0	—
b × c	0	1	0	0	—
a × b × c	7.70	2	3.85	3.29	$< {.05 \atop .01}$
Exper. error	76.91	66	1.17		
Total	213.57	83			

(Total, calculated directly: 213.31)

Table 17. Analysis of variance on A-quotients from reading period II.

a_1				a_2				a_3			
b_1		b_2		b_1		b_2		b_1		b_2	
c_1	c_2	c_1	c_2	c_1	c_2	c_1	c_2	c_1	c_2	c_1	c_2
120	101	121	137	98	178	159	149	125	150	177	124
116	109	127	93	104	166	123	121	131	148	174	166
118	100	149	108	121	144	188	202	110	126	134	212
75	118	123	104	107	160	138	127	182	145	144	176
112	95	94	99	102	147	129	220	115	157	169	148
84	121	99	154	132	98	163	166	123	151	163	165

Source of variance	Sum of squares	Df	Mean square	F	p
Replications	1007.3	5	201.5	0.35	$>.20$
a: Reading ability	20763.8	2	10381.9	18.13	$<.001$
b: Understandability of the text	7938.0	1	7938.0	13.86	$<.001$
c: Readability of the text	2640.2	1	2640.2	4.61	$<\genfrac{}{}{0pt}{}{.05}{.01}$
Interactions:					
a $\times$ b	829.8	2	414.9	0.72	$>.20$
a $\times$ c	2078.1	2	1039.1	1.81	$<\genfrac{}{}{0pt}{}{.20}{.10}$
b $\times$ c	813.4	1	813.4	1.42	$>.20$
a $\times$ b $\times$ c	261.7	2	130.9	0.23	$>.20$
Exper. error	31503.1	55	572.8		
Total	67835.4	71			

(Total, calculated directly: 67836.3)

9*

Table 18. Analysis of variance on A-differences from reading period II.

	a_1				a_2				a_3			
	b_1		b_2		b_1		b_2		b_1		b_2	
c_1	c_2	c_1	c_2	c_1	c_2	c_1	c_2	c_1	c_2	c_1	c_2
---	---	---	---	---	---	---	---	---	---	---	---
143	77	95	155	69	161	251	150	89	171	183	169
97	92	120	105	87	188	105	126	132	225	169	402
118	75	186	78	112	176	319	180	106	162	226	363
113	108	63	68	95	175	223	152	172	174	189	215
17	60	122	56	81	247	135	344	116	228	189	206
0	104	71	192	145	69	220	159	115	274	228	271

Source of variance	Sum of squares	Df	Mean square	F	p
Replications	7875.0	5	1575.0	0.49	$> .20$
a: Reading ability	130978.5	2	65489.3	20.24	$< .001$
b: Understandability of the text	50774.7	1	50774.7	15.69	$< .001$
c: Readability of the next	21910.7	1	21910.7	6.77	$< \begin{matrix} .01 \\ .001 \end{matrix}$
Interactions:					
a × b	6977.3	2	3488.7	1.08	$> .20$
a × c	18787.9	2	9393.9	2.90	$< \begin{matrix} .10 \\ .05 \end{matrix}$
b × c	6086.2	1	6086.2	1.88	$< \begin{matrix} .20 \\ .10 \end{matrix}$
a × b × c	7603.9	2	3801.9	1.18	$> .20$
Exper. error	177932.0	55	3235.1		
Total	428926.2	71			

(Total, calculated directly: 428926.0)

132

Table 19. p-values of all the sources of variance from the analyses of variance appearing in Tables 14-18.

	a	b	c	a×b	a×c	b×c	a×b×c
I. (A-quot.)	$<.001$	$<\substack{.05\\.01}$	$<\substack{.01\\.001}$	$>.20$	$>.20$	$>.20$	$<\substack{.05\\.01}$
II. (A-quot.)	$<.001$	$<\substack{.05\\.01}$	$<\substack{.01\\.001}$	—*)	—*)	—*)	$=.05$
III. (A-diff.)	$<.001$	$=.05$	$<\substack{.20\\.10}$	$>.20$	$=.10$	$>.20$	$>.20$
IV. (A-quot.)	$<.001$	$<.001$	$<\substack{.05\\.01}$	$>.20$	$<\substack{.20\\.10}$	$>.20$	$>.20$
V. (A-diff.)	$<.001$	$<.001$	$<\substack{.01\\.001}$	$>.20$	$<\substack{.10\\.05}$	$<\substack{.20\\.10}$	$>.20$

*) sum of squares $= 0$

As indicated above, all the p-values in variable a are highly significant; in variable b they are significant; and they are also significant in variable c yet with one exception (III). As regards the p-values of the interactions, quite the opposite is the case: only in one case of sixteen[1] does a significant p-value appear.

This almost total absence of significant interaction values facilitates the interpretation of the analyses of variance, since such an absence makes a supposition indicating the additivity of the main effects more justifiable.

A simple way of controlling the dimensionality of the measurements from reading periods I and II, in order to determine whether or not it is possible to bring them together, is to investigate the direction of the changes in bioelectric activity, when the activity values from the first reading period are com-

---

[1] The row indicated by II in table 19 is not included in this statement, as the figures indicated in that row have resulted from a calculation which was made for a special purpose, viz., to test whether or not there were any changes in the analysis of variance when the variances of the A-quotients were made more homogeneous.

Table 20. Testing the changes in silent speech in transitions from one text to another: 1.

Category of reading ability and measure of activity	p-values of the four different transitions			
	1 $H_a: + > \frac{1}{2}$	2 $H_a: - > \frac{1}{2}$	3 $H_a: + > \frac{1}{2}$	4 $H_a: - > \frac{1}{2}$
Good readers				
A-quotient	.039*	.073	.046*	.132
A-difference	.039*	.073	.046*	.132
Medium readers				
A-quotient	.003**	.019*	.006**	.046*
A-difference	.003**	.019*	.006**	.046*
Poor readers				
A-quotient	.090	.003**	.194	.002**
A-difference	.033*	.003**	.194	.033*

pared with those from the second for the same subject. In this transition, the following changes in the texts used occur:

Reading period I	Reading period II
Easy and clear text ⟶	Difficult and blurred text
Easy and blurred text ⟶	Difficult and clear text
Difficult and clear text ⟶	Easy and blurred text
Difficult and blurred text ⟶	Easy and clear text.

As the interaction values for the understandability and the readability of the texts (b × c) are insignificant, as indicated in Table 19, it seems reasonable, without taking into consideration the combinations just given, to calculate whether there are changes in activity significantly above or below 0 during the following four transitions:

1. transition from easy to difficult text
2. transition from difficult to easy text
3. transition from clear to blurred text
4. transition from blurred to clear text.

The changes were recorded only as + or —, and the null hypothesis was tested by means of the binomial test. In this test, the three reading ability categories were investigated separately. Table 20, seen on p. 134, gives the p-values for the occurrence of the expected results, according to the alternative hypothesis; these p-values, for each transition, are given for the three reading ability groups separately.

As the number of subjects on which these calculations are based varies between 9 and 14, the tendency must be considered clearly to favor the alternative hypothesis; of the total of 24 p-values, seven are significant under the .01 level and an additional 10, at or below the .05 level. Further, if the three reading ability categories are considered jointly, we find that we may, in all four cases, reject the null hypothesis with a certainty at or below the .01 level:

Table 21. Testing the changes in silent speech in transitions from one text to another: 2.

Totals	p-values of the four different transitions			
	1	2	3	4
A-quotient	.003**	.002**	.015*	.009**
A-difference	.0015**	.002**	.015*	.01**

These values permit us to state that for every one of the subjects for whom we have data from both the first and second reading periods (n = 77), there seem to be changes in the electric activity in the mylohyoid muscle which may be interpreted in the same way as were the results from the analyses of variance, i.e., that this activity increases upon transition from an easy to a difficult text as well as upon transition from a clear to a blurred text, and that it decreases upon transitions in the reversed direction. In other words, the processes being measured appear to be both one-dimensional and reversible.

Coefficients of correlation between silent speech and the results in several tests of reading ability as well as in tests of other abilities had already been obtained in an earlier investigation performed during the 1957-1958 school year, with 450 pupils from the fourth grade of the elementary schools in Stockholm as subjects. The teachers whose classes were covered by this investigation made records on every one of the subjects, as regarded the following symptoms of poor reading:

1. Silent speech, i.e., movements of the lips or other parts of the mouth, or of the tongue.
2. Turning of the head during reading; i.e., eye-movements were partially replaced by movements of the head.
3. Pointing with a finger or some object at the line of text being read.

For the calculations which followed in due course, the notations of the teachers appeared in the records of the subjects as "shows" or "does not show" signs of the three symptoms indicated above, respectively. The teachers' notations also provided for quantification (in a five-point rating scale), but since the teachers might have used varying norms as bases for these notations, despite advance group training, it was considered preferable simply to dichotomize each of the three variables indicated above. They were then correlated with the following variables (r_{bis}):

a-e) results in standardized achievement tests:

    a) reading comprehension
    b) rate of reading
    c) vocabulary
    d) book information (reading of tables of contents and other tables, graphs, reference lists, indexes; how to skim a book; and similar skills)
    e) total score (weighted sum of a-d)

f) results in an intelligence test
g) school grades (all academic subjects except reading).

The coefficients of correlation thus obtained are indicated in the table which follows.

Table 22. Coefficients of correlation between silent speech and certain other variables in elementary school subjects.

	1	2	3
a)	—.47 ± .06	—.51 ± .05	—.56 ± .065
b)	—.45 ± .06	—.43 ± .055	—.40 ± .08
c)	—.27 ± .06	—.27 ± .07	—.23 ± .08
d)	—.18 ± .07	—.13 ± .06	—.15 ± .08
e)	—.37 ± .06	—.40 ± .056	—.41 ± .075
f)	—.14 ± .07	—.20 ± .06	—.16 ± .09
g)	—.35 ± .06	—.33 ± .06	—.32 ± .08

Underlined r_{bis}-values indicate coefficients which deviate significantly from 0 at the .01 level. The remaining coefficients deviate just barely or not at all from 0.

The intercorrelations between the three variables indicated on p. 136, i.e., silent speech, turning of the head and pointing, were, as shown by the following figures, relatively low:

silent speech—turning of the head $\varphi = .37;\ \varphi$ max. $= .75$
turning of the head—pointing $\varphi = .19;\ \varphi$ max. $= .51$
silent speech—pointing $\varphi = .21;\ \varphi$ max. $= .71$.

The common variances were thus very small, and the stability of the values in the rows of Table 22 is not merely spurious.

If we compare the coefficients of correlation which appear in the first column of Table 22, i.e., those corcerning silent speech, with data obtained when silent speech was similarly correlated

137

with equivalent tests performed by students in the Stockholm investigation, we find similar values.

Table 23. Coefficients of correlation between silent speech and the reading variables: the Stockholm investigation.

	Reading comprehension	Rate of reading	Vocabulary	F II	Total (weighted sum)
A-quotient I[1]	—.44	—.43	—.34	—.34	—.57
A-difference I	—.50	—.42	—.33	—.30	—.57
A-quotient II[1]	—.27	—.38	—.22	—.26	—.45
A-difference II	—.28	—.36	—.20	—.28	—.46

When the correlations between silent speech and the results of the intelligence test used in the Stockholm investigation were calculated, the following coefficients were obtained.

Table 24. Coefficients of correlation between silent speech and the intelligence test results: the Stockholm investigation.

	I-points
A-quotient I[1]	—.25
A-difference I	—.33
A-quotient II[1]	—.23
A-difference II	—.36

At the same time as the Stockholm investigation, an ophthalmographic control of the eye movements in reading was carried out. By way of comparison, it may be mentioned that the average number of fixatons and regressions per line[2] of text calculated from the graphs obtained in this control gave the following coefficients of correlation, for the same test variables as those given in Table 23 above (n = 84).

---

[1] The Roman numerals I and II refer to reading periods I and II, respectively ($n_I = 84$; $n_{II} = 72$).

[2] See also p. 155.

Table 25. Coefficients of correlation between eye-movement variables and the reading variables: the Stockholm investigation.

	Reading comprehension	Rate of reading	Vocabulary	F II	Total	I-points
$M_{fix/line}$	—.26	—.29	—.17	—.19	—.31	—.18
$M_{regress/line}$	—.21	—.20	—.15	—.12	—.28	—.12

These coefficients are, obviously, consistently lower than the corresponding values for silent speech, though ophthalmographic control of eye movements in reading is an aid which has long been used in connection with the diagnosis of reading ability.

Between the ophthalmographic variables, on the one hand, and the A-quotients and A-differences on the other, there is a rather weak positive relationship:

Table 26. Coefficients of correlation between eye-movement variables and silent speech: the Stockholm investigation.

	A-quotient I	A-quotient II	A-diff. I	A-diff. II
$M_{fix/line}$	.16	.15	.21	.11
$M_{regress/line}$	.06	.11	.22	.19

These data concerning the relationship between our ophthalmographic variables and our silent speech variables will be commented on in Appendix A, p. 155 et seqq.

CHAPTER 8

DISCUSSION AND CONCLUSIONS

In the investigation conducted in Denmark, it was shown that reading causes increases in the electric activity in both the vocal and mylohyoid muscles. The simplified manner of calculating which was employed on the recordings from the vocal muscle in that investigation could of course have been used in the material of the Stockholm investigation, as well.

In order, however, to obtain as reliable quantifications as possible of the activity variable in the Stockholm investigation, a more time-consuming technique was chosen. Sampling of a number of observations was carried out along the integrated activity curve, so that, for a ten-second period, 50 separate measurements of the activity during relaxation and during reading, respectively, were obtained. These measurements were expressed in mm. above the zero line of the curve. Transformation into μV could be performed easily, as the amplification in the whole registering device is known. However, since some sort of derived data, rather than the original measurements, had to be used (see p. 40 et seqq.) as a measure of the dependent variable, such a transformation was considered not to serve any purpose.

The question then was which measure of the electric activity in the mylohyoid muscle during reading was the most appropriate for use. The two measures which we had calculated and from which we had to choose were the A-quotients and the A-differences, and of these the A-quotients seem preferable for comparisons between different subjects, as they relate the activity during reading to the original impulse amplitude, which the A-differences fail to do.

If we examine the original distributions of these two activity variables, we find that the lower limits of the activity quotients, as shown in the tables on pp. 128 and 131 are less than 100, which means that there are included in the material cases where

140

the activity during relaxation is higher than that during reading. Thus, some of the activity differences are negative. In order to avoid these negative figures, however, we have added to all original values a constant which is equivalent to the highest negative value.

Seven good readers from reading period I and seven good readers and two medium readers from reading period II produced electromyograms where the activity during relaxation was higher than that during reading.[1] A possible explanation of the fact that this phenomenon did not occur at all among the poor readers follows.

Weddell, Feinstein and Pattle (op. cit.) name some muscles that are generally difficult to relax. The mylohyoids must be reckoned among these, since the hyoid bone and thus the larynx partly, as well, are suspended from them. In addition to this relative relaxation activity (a) which must, then, occur in the mylohyoid muscle, there will very likely be activity resulting from a reduction in the subject's ability to relax due to the stress of the experimental situation. This additional activity (b), which may thus be viewed as experimentally induced, must be greater, because of the fact that it is not a single muscle only which is to be relaxed, but a whole part of the face (the lower jaw, the lips and the tongue). The relevant activity which is added during reading, i.e., the silent speech, may be indicated by (c). When the subject switches from relaxation to reading, a minor part (δb) disappears from the experimentally induced activity (b), presumably due to the fact that the reading task diverts somewhat the attention of the subject.[2] The two experimental situations may thus be indicated as follows.

---

[1] Of the seven good readers here referred to in reading period II, four were among those mentioned in the same connection for reading period I, as well.

[2] Support for this assumption, though the matter has not been studied systematically, is provided by the fact that when the subjects were spoken to by the experimenter during the experiment, the relaxation activity sank and remained low as long as the subjects in question were listening.

Activity during relaxation	Activity during reading
or	or
Initial Activity	Final Activity
$a + b = A_i$	$a + (b - \delta b) + c = A_f$ (i)

In the cases where $A_i > A_f$, the reason is that $\delta b > c$. Nor is this an absurdity, in the case of a good reader who is reading an easy and clear text, in which instance (c) may be supposed to approach 0.

Proceeding from the above two formulas of the two main experimental situations, we can derive formulas for the activity differences and activity quotients. The basic formula for A_f should, however, first be rewritten, as follows:

$$A_f = a + b\,(1 - \delta) + c. \qquad (ii)$$

The activity difference may then be expressed:

$$a + b\,(1 - \delta) + c - (a + b)$$

or

$$c - b \cdot \delta, \qquad (iii)$$

and thus gives us the best possible numerical approximation of the activity increment during reading.

The formula for the activity quotient is as follows:

$$\frac{a + b\,(1 - \delta) + c}{a + b}$$

or

$$1 + \frac{c - b \cdot \delta}{a + b} \qquad (iv)$$

The algebraic representation of the activity difference thus appears here as the numerator. If this is indicated by (d), we then obtain, through substitution in formula (iv), and as the final formula for the activity quotient, the following:

$$1 + \frac{d}{a + b}. \qquad (v)$$

The activity quotient is thus a relative difference, a measure of $c - b \cdot \delta$, but related to the original impulse amplitude, the initial activity A_i. This appears to indicate that the A-quotients are the most correct measures of the dependent variable, since the A-differences are dependent on the amplitude of the initial impulses just as are the directly registered activity values. However, until the curve for this state of dependence is known, it is impossible to state with assurance which of the two measures *is* the most correct one. Regarding the curve in question, we lack information, and furthermore no such dependence could be discovered in our experimental results. The coefficient of correlation there between the activity differences and the initial activity was calculated to be .11 ± .08. If we consider, further, that the correlation between the A-quotients and the A-differences is as high as .82 ± .03, as well as the fact that the correlations between the A-quotients and different reading variables, on the one hand, and on the other, those between the A-differences and the same reading variables show such great similarity (see Table 23 on p. 138), it appears to be of very little importance which of the two measures are chosen as a basis for further calculations in the present investigation. Therefore, the A-differences are to be preferred, as they are the less complicated measures of the two.

If, all the same, the A-quotients are also used for analysis of variance, the results should be about the same as those obtained on the basis of the A-differences. Such is also the case (see pp. 128-132 and the summary table on p. 133). Even though the analyses of variance based on the A-quotients have not provided any new information, they have been brought in to strengthen the statements concerning Hypothesis C (see p. 145).

Yet it may still be asked in connection with the treatment of the present material, why it is possible to use both these measurements of activity when only the A-quotients relate the measured activity during reading to the amplitudes of the initial impulses. The explanation may well be that it is only when the electrode is inserted in such a manner that it registers impulses from only one or from but a few functioning motor units that the absolute amplitudes of the impulses have any real effect on the magnitude of the A-differences. When, on the other hand, the electrode is so inserted that it picks up impulses from a large number of motor units, there is an equalization in amplitude of the separate initial activities of the individual experimental subjects. If the activity differences are then related to the initial activity in the same manner as in the calculation of the activity quotients, the corrections of the difference values are very small. The likelihood that the electrode will be so inserted that it picks up impulses from a single motor unit, or a few motor units only, is very small in muscles like the mylohyoids.

Regardless of these considerations however, we can state that *activity quotients and activity differences have been proved to be equally useful with the material of and for the specific purposes of the present investigation.*

Testing the Experimental Hypotheses

On page 109 the following hypotheses were set:

A. Good readers engage in less silent speech than do poor readers.
B. The reading of an easy text results in less silent speech than does the reading of a difficult one.
C. The reading of a clear text results in less silent speech than does the reading of a blurred one.

Hypothesis A

In all our analyses of variance, there occur differences in means between the three blocks, a_1, a_2 and a_3 that are significantly greater than are the differences in variance within any one of these blocks. This means that, among our subjects, low reading scores and high silent speech values occur together.

The results are the same whether A-quotients or A-differences are used as a basis for calculations. This is fully in agreement with Hypothesis A, i.e., although individuals of approximately the same age, intelligence and educational background have been compared, the good readers engage in less silent speech than do the poor readers.

Hypothesis B

Also as regards variable b, there are, in all the analyses of variance, differences in means which are significantly greater between the groups of subjects who were given treatment b_1, on the one hand, and the groups who were given treatment b_2, on the other, than there are within these groups. This means that those of our subjects who were given treatment b_1 showed significantly less silent speech than did those who were given treatment b_2. Here again the results are the same whether the calculations are based on the activity quotients or on the activity differences. These experimental results are fully in agreement with Hypotheses B, i.e., the reading of the easy text has resulted in less silent speech than has the reading of the difficult one.

Hypothesis C

Concerning variable c, there are, in three of the four analyses of variance, differences in means which are significantly greater between the groups of subjects who were given treatment c_1, on the one hand, and the groups who were given c_2, on the other, than there are within these groups. In one of the analyses of variance based on activity differences, however, this significantly greater difference between the groups is lacking. Thus we cannot speak with the same degree of certainty concerning the truth of Hypothesis C as in the cases of the other two hypotheses. Yet we can state that even in the one exceptional case just mentioned, the groups which were given treatment c_1 showed less silent speech than did those given treatment c_2. Thus, Hypothesis C is also strongly supported by the experimental results. This means that the reading of a clear text very likely gives rise to less silent speech than does the reading of a blurred one.

It is possible that the set level of significance would also have been reached in the fourth case, that is the exceptional one, above, if the differences in clearness between the two texts used had been greater. Yet pilot studies which had been carried out, with varying difficulty intervals between the texts which were being considered for use in treatments c_1 and c_2, had indicated that the difficulty interval actually chosen was sufficient. Obtaining a proper balance here is a very delicate matter, since too great an interval will surely result in other qualifications than pure reading ability influencing the reading comprehension scores.

In the next section of the present chapter, the theories and views on silent speech which were discussed in Chapter 6 will be treated. Our experimental results now enable us to form more decisive opinions concerning these theories and views. In this discussion, our results concerning understandability and readability will be used jointly, which we believe compensates for the small degree of uncertainty concerning hypothesis C.

Bearings of the Present Experimental Results
on Earlier Theories

A most important question here is to what extent we have the possibility of generalizing on the basis of our experimental results. For in order to take a decided position regarding the theories discussed earlier, we must be able to generalize in three different respects, viz.:

a) from activity in the mylohyoid muscle to silent speech in general;
b) from our experimental reading situation to reading generally;
c) from our experimental subjects to larger groups of people.

146

On the basis of our definition of silent speech (p. 14), however, it is questionable whether requirement a) above really applies. Since silent speech is there defined as "all instances of movement in the speech muscles in accompaniment with reading...," it may be deemed sufficient to state that the mylohyoids are muscles included in the wide concept "the organ of speech," as defined on p. 46. Increased activity in the mylohyoid muscle during reading *is* thus silent speech in reading. Furthermore, direct comparisons which have been made between the activity of this muscle and that of the vocal muscle, as well as indirect comparisons with the posterior cricoarytenoid muscle (see p. 65 ff.), have indicated such a degree of simultaneity in the work of the three muscles that generalization according to a) above, if such should be considered requisite, is, after all, justified.

Our experimental situation, as depicted in Fig. 24, p. 119, does not, of course, constitute a normal reading situation. Yet the discomfort resulting from an electrode inserted into the mylohyoid muscle is so small that it cannot render the experimental situation inadequate. However, it is clear that in making generalizations based on experiments of this kind, a certain degree of caution is necessary.

Concerning our experimental subjects, there is nothing to indicate that their mean intelligence test and reading test scores differ from those of that larger population from which these subjects were taken. They were, however, not drawn from this population at random. Those new students at the University of Stockholm in the fall of 1958 who attended a lecture on the techniques of reading were told that those who wished might apply for a check-up on their reading ability. From the students who registered for this check-up, those who were actually to participate in the experiment were then randomly selected. A systematic error could thus have affected the sampling already on the occasion of the original registration by the students. Yet, as stated above, when the reading scores of our subjects were compared with those recorded in altogether different connections from other similar groups of students,[1] no significant differences were obtained.

The borders between the three categories of reading ability in the present experiment were obtained by placing an equal number of subjects in each of the groups, i.e., good, medium and poor readers. This manner of dividing up the subjects very nearly coincides with a limiting at $\pm 0.4\,\sigma$ (see Fig. 22). The reading scores of our experimental subjects, as stated above, seem not to deviate from those found in samples from other similar groups. This means that we may expect to get similar results in other samples of university students, as well, if the limits are set at approximately $\pm 0.4\,\sigma$. If this limiting were to be done at exactly $\pm 0.4\,\sigma$, in a normal distribution, slightly more than 31 percent of the material would fall within these limits. The actual limiting, in the case of our material, was done a bit outside $\pm 0.4\,\sigma$, thus taking in $33\frac{1}{3}$ percent of the distribution. In other words, it should be possible, from our experimental results, to generalize regarding university students of approximately the same age and with the same intelligence and educational background as our subjects.

Can such students be thought to constitute a special group as regards reading ability? In so far as their educational background is concerned, there is nothing to support a hypothesis that such is the case. They have been given conventional reading instruction during their elementary school years. At no

---

[1] The tests given these other groups of students and from which scores have been noted for comparisons with the material of the present investigation included reading tests given to the students who attended a course in educational psychology for future secondary school teachers and to university undergraduates studying educational psychology; scores made on an intelligence test given to the students in the course for future secondary school teachers were also used for comparison. Means in z-scores and sampling errors of the means are as follows:

	Exp. group	Comp. group
	(n = 84)	(n = 37)
reading comprehension	.01 ± .11	.004 ± .16
rate of reading	.09 ± .10	.116 ± .11
vocabulary	.105 ± .09	—.012 ± .16
L II	.021 ± .09	.06 ± .14
	(n = 84)	(n = 85)
intelligence	.052 ± .25	.003 ± .11

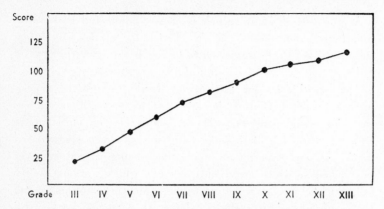

Fig. 27. *Average growth in reading ability as measured by total comprehension score in Chicago Reading Test D, Form 2 (grades III to XIII).*

level of their school studies have they been given special reading instruction or training. Nor, if we regard the investigations which have been carried out concerning the development of reading ability, do we find anything to indicate that such students constitute any sort of special group. Studies with a longitudinal approach are admittedly lacking. However, the cross-sectional studies which have been made all demonstrate that the average growth in total reading ability, as well as in reading comprehension, is a continuous process (Fig. 27). Gray (1948) concludes a discussion of the growth curve shown in this figure, and of other similar curves, as follows (p. 41):

An analysis of the larger body of evidence from which the examples were taken justifies the following conclusions: first, growth in reading ability, considered as a whole, is continuous and more or less equally paced from the primary school through college; second, the rate of progress varies widely among groups and individuals; third, whereas practically all major reading attitudes and skills function from the beginning, they mature at different times; fourth, growth in the elementary grades is most prominent in those aspects of recognition, comprehension and speed which underlie all reading activities; and, fifth, growth is most prominent at the high-school and college level in the more mature types of interpretation, critical reaction, and integration involved in efficient reading.

10 *Edfeldt*

As the use of silent speech is clearly connected with those functions which mature in the elementary grades, no differences in type can be supposed to occur, in this regard, between different categories of reading ability at later levels.

The possibilities for generalizing from the present experimental results may thus be extended to cover other readers than university students who are similar in age, intelligence and educationel background to the subjects who participated in the present experiment. Such generalizing should however be limited so as to cover only persons whose reading ability falls within the range of variation which was found among these subjects. This excludes, above all, persons who are still learning to read and persons whose reading ability corresponds to that which is normally found among pupils during the first three or four years of elementary school.

It must be pointed out, however, that such wide generalization is only valid provided university freshmen, approximately 22 years of age,[1] do not constitute a special group as regards reading ability. In connection with the standardizing of reading tests and during courses in the techniques of reading with adult students, several different categories of pupils have been tested with the same battery of tests as was used in connection with the present experiment. Among those so tested were technical students, students of economics, administrative personnel at different levels both within industry and state departments and members of study circles organized by the Laborers' Educational Association and other organizations. The differences noted between these various groups have, in all instances, been of the same kind as those noted within each specific group. No qualitative group differences, i.e., differences indicating different structures in the reading ability of the respective groups of pupils, have been found. This fact, it is believed, gives additional support to our widest generalizations.

In summary, on the basis of the present experimental data,

---

[1] Partly as a result of the structure of the Swedish educational system, university studies are generally commenced in Sweden somewhat later than in some other countries.

direct statements can be made concerning silent speech in accompaniment with the reading of 22-year-old freshmen at the University of Stockholm. It does not seem likely, however, that the structure of the reading ability of this group differs qualitatively from that of other categories of readers. Our conclusions therefore apply to all persons who have achieved a reading ability which corresponds to or surpasses that normally possessed by a pupil who has completed the third or fourth year of elementary school.

In Chapter 6, the existent theories and views concerning silent speech in reading were discussed. This discussion may now be carried further.

Already in Part I, it was shown that silent speech *probably* occurs during all reading. It is, however, not possible to state categorically that such is the case, as some of the good readers showed less activity during reading than during relaxation. In these cases, it is impossible to say what is silent speech and what is activity of some other kind in the muscle in question. It may be that that part of the total activity measured in the mylohyoid muscle which is induced by reading, i.e., the silent speech, approaches zero in the case of some good readers.

However, as it was demonstrated that silent speech increased even in the cases of the best readers when the text became more difficult either in content (Hypothesis B) or due to its typography (Hypothesis C), it is clear that spontaneous silent speech *can* occur in all readers.

Further, since silent speech increases in all categories of reading ability when a more difficult text is read, it is evident that such increases also occur in connection with the reading of more difficult passages, or even single words which are more difficult, which passages and words are almost always to be found even in very easy textual material. It therefore seems justifiable to say that *silent speech occurs in the reading of all people*. This is true despite the fact that activity in the speech musculature might cease altogether during the reading of very easy words or passages in the text. This is also true despite

151

the fact that there are persons in whom the speech musculature is paralyzed yet who can nevertheless read, for silent speech is not a physiological requirement in reading.

The causes of silent speech and its effects may be treated together in this discussion. Since our experimental results were fully in agreement with Hypothesis A we can state that silent speech occurs more during the reading of poor readers than it does during that of good readers. Yet the very strong support obtained for Hypotheses B and C indicates that even very good readers engage in increased amounts of silent speech if the texts read are very demanding on their reading ability. *It is then impossible to view silent speech as a habit detrimental to reading.* Both the poorer reading performance and the increase in silent speech which may well accompany it are rather results of the same factor, viz., the fact that the text is in some respect more difficult to handle. The increase in silent speech may therefore be viewed as an indication that a person's reading ability does not enable him to grasp what he is reading without difficulty.

It may then be appropriate to inquire why silent speech increases when a reader has difficulty in grasping the content of a text. Is the silent speech a real aid, or is it a phenomenon of regression of the kind to be found in other areas of human behavior? This question cannot be answered on the basis of the results of the present investigation.

Yet these results clearly seem to prove that silent speech cannot have a detrimental effect on reading performance. Already in Chapter 6, it was pointed out, as well, that nothing is known concerning reading without silent speech. If these facts are united, it seems clear that the advisability of direct attempts to eliminate silent speech is highly dubious. In agreement with Fryer (op. cit.), the present writer believes such attempts to be dubious to such a degree that it would be better to discard them totally, especially since experience seems to indicate that other kinds of remedial reading both improve reading ability and, for anyone who may be interested, result in a decrease in the occurrence of silent speech, as well.

CHAPTER 9

SUMMARY

The purpose of this investigation has been to determine whether there exists any relationship between a person's reading ability and the occurrence of silent speech in that person. By silent speech, we mean here "all instances of movement in the speech muscles in accompaniment with reading or other forms of mental activity." The electromyographic method was the one chosen for studying this subject. The basic methodological experiment was performed in order to ascertain that it was possible to register electromyographically silent speech in reading. The main experiment was performed on 84 students during their first term of study at the University of Stockholm. In this experiment, the following three hypotheses were tested:

A. Good readers engage in less silent speech than do poor readers.
B. The reading of an easy text results in less silent speech than does the reading of a difficult one.
C. The reading of a clear text results in less silent speech than does the reading of a blurred one.

Two different measures of silent speech were calculated, viz., the differences between activity during relaxation and activity during reading (activity differences) and those same differences stated in relation to the amplitude of the original impulses, i.e., in relation to the activity during relaxation (activity quotients). Both of these measures proved to be equally usable in our experiment as measures of the dependent variable.

The testing of the above hypotheses, which was carried out by means of the analysis of variance, showed our experimental results to be fully in agreement with Hypotheses A and B, while Hypothesis C was strongly supported. This means, as regards Hypothesis A, that more silent speech occurs during reading in a poor reader than in a good reader. The interpretation of Hypothesis B is that as the content of a text becomes more difficult, silent speech increases in all readers. Hypothesis C, finally, is interpreted to indicate the great likelihood that silent speech also increases in all readers when the text is less clear, as, for example, in the case of the reading of a third or fourth carbon copy of typewritten material.

It appears possible to generalize from the results obtained for the subjects of this experiment to all persons whose reading ability falls within the limits of the range of variation shown by these experimental subjects.

On the basis of the present experimental results, earlier theories concerning silent speech in reading may be judged. These theories often appear to have been constructed afterwards, in order to justify some already adopted form of remedial reading. In opposition to most of these theories, we wish to claim that silent speech occurs in the reading of all persons.

Further, it is evident that silent speech cannot be a habit which is, in itself, detrimental to the reading performance. It is a symptom of a reader's not being able to grasp the content of a text without difficulties. These difficulties may arise due to poor reading ability on the part of the reader or because the text has a low degree of understandability (i.e., is difficult in content) or of readability (i.e., is blurred, poor in typography or the like). Nothing definite can be said regarding whether silent speech actually constitutes an aid toward better reading comprehension, though it appears likely that it may do so. In any case, it seems quite clear that all kinds of training aimed at removing silent speech should be discarded. Although silent speech is a symptom of the fact that the reader is having difficulties in comprehending the text, the diagnostic value of this observation is still very doubtful. (In this latter regard, see further Appendix A.)

Appendix A

SILENT SPEECH AND THE DIAGNOSIS OF INDIVIDUAL READING ABILITY

A question which has only been touched upon earlier in this study is whether electromyographic data concerning the occurrence of silent speech in reading can be utilized for diagnostic purposes. Comparisons may be made with the photographing of eye movements during reading, since this method is generally accepted as a useful aid in reading diagnosis. The measures, for diagnosis, usually derived from an eye-movement record are, mainly, *the average number of fixations per line* and *the average number of regressions per line*. By regressions are understood, in this specific context, movements backwards, i.e., repetitions of text already read.

Concurrently with the Stockholm electromyographic investigation described in this report, an ophthalmographic study of eye-movements during reading was also performed on the subjects, and the above named measures were calculated. If the eye-movement records, on the one hand, and the activity differences obtained in the electromyographic investigation, on the other, are both correlated with the reading test scores of the subjects, the measures of silent speech show throughout higher coefficients of correlation than do the average values for fixations and regressions per line of the eye-movement record (see p. 139). Since a direct comparison between the silent speech values and the eye-movement values gives a mean coefficient of correlation as low as .18, the two kinds of values cover almost entirely different aspects of the criterion, i.e., of the reading ability.

If the relative values obtained from an electromyogram are to be used diagnostically for individual persons, there is of course a source of error in the varying ability consciously to relax the speech musculature possessed by different individuals; i.e., δb varies in size. Even temporary fluctuations in this ability surely occur in the same individual. Nor do we find the mean coefficient of correlation obtained between reading ability and silent speech, i.e., —.52, sufficient to provide reliable predictions concerning individual reading ability, if the values for silent speech are used alone. Only about 14 percent reduction in the errors of prediction is provided for by such a validity coefficient. Possibly a combination of values obtained in silent speech and eye-movement investigations might give a validity more satisfactory for the purposes of diagnosing the reading ability of individual persons. Yet a multiple correlation, corrected for bias, between the silent speech variable and the two eye-movement variables, on the one hand, and the criterion variable, i.e., the reading ability, on the other, gives in our material an increase of only three hundredths over the coefficient of correlation already obtained between silent speech and reading ability. It should be added that this applies to diagnoses concerning individuals at all levels of reading ability.

A circumstance which might render the EMG a somewhat better tool for determining differences between poor readers than for determining differences between good readers is the fact that the variability in the silent speech measures is significantly higher among the poor readers than among the good ones. Yet if the reading scores are correlated with the activity differences for the subjects within each of the three categories of reading ability, and for the two reading periods, I and II, for which calculations were made, the following coefficients of correlation are obtained.

Table 27. Coefficients of correlation between A-differences and reading scores in the reading ability groups taken separately.

Measure of activity	Good readers	Medium readers	Poor readers
A-differences, I	—.05	.22	—.18
A-differences, II	—.09	.32	—.03

None of these coefficients deviates significantly from 0. It is nevertheless possible that a *weak* relationship exists, but in such a small sample as that involved here, the margin of error is too great to permit the demonstration of significance in such a weak relationship. Support for the likelihood that the greater variability in the activity measures within the category of poor readers might provide for more dependable diagnoses than is possible in other categories of reading ability can thus not be derived from the results of this investigation.

The greater variability among the poor readers may well be due to the fact that the measured bioelectric activity is generally greater in this group. This greater activity almost certainly causes new sources of error, e.g., inter-effects between the incoming impulses. The passage of an impulse through a tissue includes different phases, e.g., a positive one and a negative one, as shown in Fig. 28 a. Of course, the impulse can be in any of its phases when it reaches the electrode and is registered. For several reasons, impulses from different motor units cannot be in the same phase when they reach the electrode. Among these reasons are the different distances traveled by the nerve impulses, different distances between the muscle fibers of the activated motor units and the electrode, and a different distribution of the end plates in the different motor units.

As a result of these phase shifts, recording errors may occur. Of these, one example will be given here, viz., what happens when impulses in opposite phases reach the electrode simultaneously, as shown in Fig. 28 b. The two shadowed phases in this figure cancel each other in the registration and what actually reach the record are the negative phase of impulse I and the positive phase of impulse II. The greater the activity is generally, i.e., the more constantly impulses reach the electrode, the greater is the probability that errors of this kind and similar kinds will occur.

Further investigation concerning this matter is, however, highly desirable, as it is, generally, in regard to the diagnostic usability of electromyographic recordings of silent speech in reading.

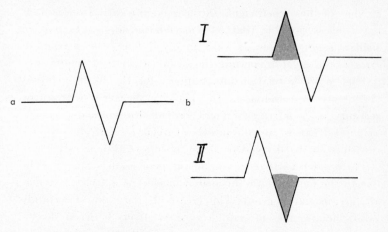

Fig. 28. Single diphasic spike potentials; (b) shows two such spike potentials in opposite phases.

In the testing of persons' reading ability, a number of different tests are always used, designed to measure different aspects of that ability. It seems not unreasonable to suppose that one or more of these sub-categories of ability might be highly correlated with silent speech. It is, however, questionable whether it is realistic to think of reading ability as the sum, or weighted sum, of a number of functioning sub-abilities. The division, on the occasion of the testing of reading ability, into rate of reading, reading comprehension, vocabulary and other categories may rather be deemed a necessity due to the difficulties which arise when an attempt is made to measure reading ability as a whole. Logically, however, it seems that the most adequate measure of reading ability is the rate of reading comprehension, i.e., the speed with which a person grasps 100 percent (or some other given percentage) of the content of the text read. This view renders less interesting the correlations given on pp. 137-138 between the scores on tests of different aspects of reading ability, on the one hand, and silent speech, on the other.

A further consideration of the relationship between silent speech in reading and intelligence might, however, be of interest.

158

If the mean values for the coefficients of correlation given in the columns headed "Total (weighted sum)" and "I-points" in Tables 23 and 24, respectively, on pp. 138-139 are calculated, these mean values can then be used as a basis for certain further calculations. For these further calculations, we need as well the coefficient of correlation between the intelligence points and the total reading ability.

$r_{ss}/$reading ability (total) $\qquad = -.52$ (mean value from Table 23, p. 138)

$r_{ss}/$I-points $\qquad = -.28$ (mean value from Table 24, p. 139)

$r_{\text{I-points}}/$reading ability (total)$= \quad .28$

If the effects of intelligence are partialized from the relationship between silent speech and reading ability, the numerical value of this relationship is altered by only four hundredths, i.e., to —.48.

Corresponding data can be given for the elementary school subjects mentioned on p. 136.

$$r_{ss}/\text{reading ability (total)} \qquad = -.37$$
$$r_{ss}/\text{I-points} \qquad = -.14$$
$$r_{\text{I-points}}/\text{reading ability (total)} = \quad .73[1]$$

If the effects of intelligence are partialized here, as above, from the relationship between silent speech and the total reading ability, the change in this relationship amounts to two hundredths, i.e., the coefficient becomes — .39.

Neither concerning the university students nor the elementary school children, then, did the intelligence of the subjects have any bearing on the occurrence of silent speech in reading.

---

[1] In the group of university students, highly homogeneous as it is with regard to intelligence, the I-points variable has, as expected, very little bearing on reading ability as compared with its bearing in the group of school children, where practically the whole original variability in the intelligence variable is still present.

REFERENCES

ABELL, ADELAIDE, M. (1894) Rapid Reading: Advantage and Methods. *Educ. Rev.*, 8, 283-285.

ADRIAN, E. D. & BRONK, D. W. (1929) The Discharge of Impulses in Motor Nerve Fibres. Part II: The Frequency of Discharge in Reflex and Voluntary Contractions. *J. Physiol.*, 67, 119-151.

ANDERSON, I. H. & DEARBORN, W. F. (1952) *The Psychology of Teaching Reading.* New York: Ronald Press.

ANDERSON, I. H. & SWANSON, D. E. (1937) Common Factors in Eye-movement in Silent and Oral Reading. *Psychol. Monogr.*, 48: 3, 61-69.

BAIN, ALEXANDER (1868) *The Senses and the Intellect.* (Third edition.) London: Longmans, Green, and Co.

BALLET, GILBERT (1886) *Le Langage Intérieur.* Paris: Ancienne Libraire Germer Baillière et Cⁱᵉ.

BAYLE, EVALYN (1942) The Nature and Causes of Regressive Movements in Reading. *J. exp. Education*, 11, 16-36.

BETTS, EMMETT A. (1950) *Foundations of Reading Instruction.* New York: American Book Company.

BIRD, C. & BEERS, F. S. (1933) Maximum and Minimum Inner Speech in Reading. *J. appl. Psych.*, 17, 182-187.

BOND, G. L. & BOND, E. (1952) *Developmental Reading in High School.* New York: Macmillan.

BOND, G. L. & TINKER, M. A. (1957) *Reading Difficulties: Their Diagnosis and Correction.* New York: Appleton.

BUCHTAL, FRITZ (1957) *An Introduction to Electromyography.* Copenhagen: Gyldendal.

BUSWELL, G. T. (1945) *Non-Oral Reading: A Study of Its Use in the Chicago Public Schools.* Supplementary Educational Monographs, No. 60. Chicago.

— (1947a) Perceptual Research and Methods of Learning. *Scientific Monthly*, 64, 521-526.

— (1947b) The Subvocalization Factor in the Improvement of Reading. *Elem. Sch. J.*, 48, 190-196.

— (1951) The Relationship Between Rate of Thinking and Rate of Reading. *School Rev.*, 59, 339-346.

CARLSÖÖ, SVEN (1952) *Nervous Coordination and Mechanical Function of the Mandibular Elevators. Acta odont. scand.*, Vol. 10, Suppl. 11.

CLARK, RUTH S. (1922) An Experimental Study of Silent Thinking. *Arch. Psychol.*, 48, 1-102.

COLE, LUELLA (1938) *The Improvement of Reading.* New York: Farrar & Rinehart.

— (1946) *The Elementary School Subjects.* New York: Rinehart.

COURTEN, H. C. (1902) Involuntary Movements of the Tongue. *Yale Psychol. Studies*, 10, 93-95.

CURTIS, H. S. (1900) Automatic Movements of the Larynx. *Amer. J. Psychol.*, 11, 237-239.

DOLCH, E. W. (1948) *A Manual for Remedial Reading.* Champaign, Illinois: Garrard Press.

DURRELL, D. D. (1940) *Improvement of Basic Reading Abilities.* New York: World Book Co.

ECCLES, J. C. & SHERRINGTON, C. S. (1930) Number and Contraction Values of Individual Motor Units Examined in Some Muscles of Limb. *Proceedings roy. Soc. B.* Vol. 106, 326-357.

EGGER, VICTOR (1881) *La Parole Intérieur.* Paris: Libraire Germer Baillière et Cie.

FAABORG-ANDERSEN, K. (1957) *Electromyographic Investigation of Intrinsic Laryngeal Muscles in Humans. Acta physiol. scand.*, Vol. 41. Suppl. 140.

FAABORG-ANDERSEN, K. & EDFELDT, Å. W. (1958) Electromyography of Intrinsic and Extrinsic Laryngeal Muscles During Silent Speech: Correlation with Reading Activity. *Acta oto-laryng.*, 49, 478-482.

FAIRBANKS, GRANT (1937) The Relation Between Eye-Movements and Voice in the Oral Reading of Good and Poor Silent Readers. *Psychol. Monogr.*, 48: 3.

FINK, B. R., BASEK, M. & EPANCHIN, V. (1956) The Mechanism of Opening of the Human Larynx. *Laryngoscope*, 66, p. 410.

FRYER, DOUGLAS H. (1941) Articulation in Automatic Mental Work. *Amer. J. Psychol.*, 54, 504-517.

GATES, ARTHUR J. (1947) *The Improvement of Reading.* New York: Macmillan.

GILSON, A. S. Jr & MILLS, W. B. (1941) Activities of Single Motor Units in Man During Slight Voluntary Efforts. *Amer. J. Physiol.*, 133, 658-669.

GJESSING, HANS-JÖRGEN (1958) *En studie av lesemodenhet ved skolegangens begynnelse.* (A Study on Reading Readiness at the Beginning of School.) Oslo: J. W. Cappelens forlag.

GRAY, C. T. (1922) *Deficiencies in Reading Ability.* Boston: Heath.

GRAY, WILLIAM S. (1948) in *Reading in the High School and College.* Forty-seventh Yearbook of the N. S. S. E., Part II. Chicago: Univ. Chicago Press.

— (1956) *The Teaching of Reading and Writing.* Paris: Unesco.

HANSEN, F. C. C. & LEHMANN, ALFR. (1895) Ueber unwillkürliches Flüstern. *Philos. Studien*, 11, 471-530.

HARRIS, ALBERT J. (1948) *How To Increase Reading Ability*. New York: Longmans & Green.

HEAD, HENRY (1926) *Aphasia and Kindred Disorders of Speech*. (2 vols.) New York: Macmillan.

HOEFFER, PAUL F. A. & PUTNAM, TRACY J. (1939) Action Potentials of Muscles in Normal Subjects. *Arch. Neurol. Psychiat.*, 42, 201-218.

HOLLINGWORTH, H. L. (1933) *Educational Psychology*. New York: Appleton.

HUEY, EDMUND B. (1908) *The Psychology and Pedagogy of Reading*. New York: Macmillan.

HUSSON, RAOUL (1955) Donées Expérimentales Nouvelles Concernant la Physiologie de la Phonation. *Exposés Annuels d'Oto-Rhino-Laryngologie*, 181-209.

HYATT, ADA V. (1943) *The Place of Oral Reading in the School Program*. New York: Teachers College, Columbia Univ.

HÄRNQVIST, K. et al. (1956) *Redogörelse för konstruktionsarbete med ett gruppintelligenstest* (A Report on the Work Involved in the Construction of a Group Intelligence Test). Stockholm: unpublished.

INGEBRIGTSEN, BRYNJULF (1938) Practical Application of Electromyography in Diagnosis of Tremor. *Acta psychiat.*, 13, 11-20.

INGLIS, W. B. (1948) The Early Stages of Reading: A Review of Recent Investigations. *Studies in Reading*. Vol. 1. London: Univ. London Press, 1-92.

INMAN, V. T., RALSTON, H. J., SAUNDERS, J. B. de C. M., FEINSTEIN, B. & WRIGHT, JR., E. W (1952) Relation of Human Electromyogram to Muscular Tension. *Electroenceph. clinical Neurophysiol.*, 4, 187-194.

JACOBSEN, EDMUND (1956) *Progressive Relaxation*. Chicago: Univ. Chicago Press. (Second edition.)

JUDD, CHARLES H. (1927) Reduction of Articulation. *Amer. J. Psychol.*, 39, 313-322.

KAINZ, FRIEDRICH (1956) *Psychologie der Sprache*. Vierter Band. Spezielle Sprachpsychologie. Stuttgart: Ferdinand Enke Verlag.

KRATIN, IO. G. (1955) K. metodike zapisi kolebaniĭ élektricheskikh potentsialov rechevoĭ muskulatory. (On a Method of Registration of Oscillations of Electric Potentials of the Speech Musculature.) *Zh. vyssh. nervn. Deiatel'*, 5:4, 591-594.

KRISTIANSEN, BIRTE B. (1958) *Læsningens psykologi*. (The Psychology of Reading.) Copenhagen: Gyldendal.

KUSSMAUL, A. (1910) *Die Störungen der Sprache*. Leipzig: Vogel.

162

LINDSLEY, DONALD B. (1935) Electrical Activity of Human Motor Units During Voluntary Contraction. *Amer. J. Physiol*, 114, 90-99.

LIPPOLD, O. C. J. (1952) The Relation Between Integrated Action Potentials in a Human Muscle and Its Isometric Tension. *J. Physiol.*, 117, 492-499.

LUCHSINGER, RICHARD (1951) *Stimmphysiologie und Stimmbildung.* Vienna: Springer-Verlag.

LULLIES, HANS (1953) *Physiologie der Stimme und Sprache* in Trendelenburg, W. & Schütz, E.: *Lehrbuch der Physiologie.* Springer-Verlag: Berlin, Göttingen, Heidelberg.

LUNDERVOLD, ARNE J. S. (1951) *Electromyographic Investigations of Position and Manner of Working in Typewriting. Acta physiol. scand.*, Vol. 24: Suppl. 84.

MAX, LOUIS WILLIAM (1934) An Experimental Study of the Motor Theory of Consciousness. I. Critique of Earlier Studies. *J. genet. Psychol.*, 11, 112-125.

— (1937) An Experimental Study of the Motor Theory of Consciousness. IV. Action-Current Responses in the Deaf During Awakening, Kinaesthetic Imagery and Abstract Thinking. *J. compar. Psychol.*, 24, 301-344.

McDADE, JAMES E. (1937) A Hypothesis for Non-Oral Reading: Argument, Experiment, and Results. *J. Educ. Res.*, 30, 489-503.

— (1941) *Essentials of Non-Oral Beginnnig Reading.* Chicago: Plymouth Press.

— (1946) *Next Steps in Non-Oral Reading.* West Palm Beach, Florida: Palm Beach Press.

— (1950) Method in Non-Oral Beginning Reading. *Elem. Sch. J.*, May, 1950, 497-501.

O'BRIEN, JOHN ANTHONY (1921) *Silent Reading.* New York: Macmillan.

OSTLE, BERNARD (1954) *Statistics in Research.* Ames, Iowa: Iowa State College Press.

PAULHAN, FR. (1886) Le Langage Intérieur et la Pensée. *Revue Philosophique*, 21, 26-58.

PETERSÉN, I. & KUGELBERG, E. (1949) Duration and Form of Action Potential in the Normal Human Muscle. *J. Neurol., Neurosurg. Psychiat.*, 12, 124-128.

PINTNER, RUDOLF (1913) Inner Speech During Silent Reading. *Psychol. Rev.*, 20, 129-153.

PIPER, H. (1912) *Electrophysiologie menschlicher Muskeln.* Berlin: Verlag von Julius Springer.

PRESSMAN, J. J. & KELEMEN, GEORGE (1955) Physiology of the Larynx. *Physiol. Rev.*, 35, 506-554.

QUANTZ, J. O. (1897) Problems in the Psychology of Reading. *Psychol. Rev. Monogr. Suppl.*, 2: 1.

163

Reading in the High School and College. (1948.) Forty-seventh Yearbook of the National Society for the Study of Education, Part II. Chicago: Univ. Chicago Press.

REED, H. B. (1916) The Existence and Function of Inner Speech in Thought Processes. *J. exp. Psychol.*, 1, 365-392.

ROBINSON, HELEN M. (1946) *Why Pupils Fail in Reading.* Chicago: Univ. Chicago Press.

— (editor) (1953) *Corrective Reading in Classroom and Clinic.* Supplementary Educational Monogr., 79. Chicago: Univ. Chicago Press.

ROGERS, MAURINE V. (1957) Comprehension in Oral and Silent Reading. *J. genet. Psychol.*, 17, 394-397.

SCHECK, M. GEORGE (1925) Involuntary Tongue Movements Under Varying Stimuli. *Proceedings of the Iowa Academy of Science, 32,* 385-391.

SCHUBERT, DELWYN G. (1957) *The Doctor Eyes the Poor Reader.* Springfield, Illinois: Thomas.

SECOR, W. B. (1900) Visual Reading: A Study in Mental Imagery. *Amer. J. Psychol.*, 11, 225-236.

SMITH, NILA B. (1934) *American Reading Instruction.* New York: Silver Burdett.

SMITH, OLIVE C. (1934) Action Potentials from Single Motor Units in Voluntary Contraction. *Amer. J. Physiol.*, 108, 629-638.

STRICKER, S. S. (1880) *Studien über die Sprachvorstellungen.* Vienna.

SWANSON, DONALD E. (1937) Common Elements in Silent and Oral Reading. *Psychol. Monogr.*, 48, 36-60.

THORSON, AGNES M. (1925) The Relation of Tongue Movements to Internal Speech. *J. exp. Psychol.*, 8, 1-32.

TINKER, MILES A. (1952) *Teaching Elementary Reading.* New York: Appleton-Century-Crofts.

TOMOR, E. (1910) Die Rolle der Muskeln beim Denken. *Archiv für die gesamte Psychol.*, 17, 362-366.

WATSON, JOHN B. (1914) *Behavior, an Introduction to Comparative Psychology.* New York: Holt.

WEDDELL, G., FEINSTEIN, B. & PATTLE, R. E. (1944) The Electrical Activity of Voluntary Muscle in Man Under Normal and Pathological Conditions. *Brain*, 67, 178-257.

WEGENER, C. F. (1941) Om bestemmelse af muskelaktionspotentialernes effektivspænding (On Electromyometri.) *Bibliotek for læger*, 133, 253-277.

WITTY, PAUL (1949) *Reading in Modern Education.* Boston: Heath.

WYCZOIKOWSKA, ANNA (1913) Theoretical and Experimental Studies in the Mechanism of Speech. *Psychol. Rev.*, 20, 448-458.

YOAKAM, GERALD A. (1928) *Reading and Study.* New York: Macmillan.